PRAISE FOR

PRETEND I'M YOUR FRIEND

"There are, I suppose, stories full of brilliance, hilarity, and longing—the stories in MB Caschetta's terrific *Pretend I'm Your Friend* are full of all these things—but I can't remember when I've read a collection so full of life. Actual life: the bad jokes, the astounding velocity, the sweetness and darkness. You will love the characters here the way you love your own family: complicatedly, with tenderness, understanding, and consternation. The only difference may be how willing—and eager—you are to introduce them to friends. Good heavens, this book is good."

—Elizabeth McCracken, author of *Thunderstruck*

"A book of youthful verve, humor, melancholy and desire. It confronts the central mysteries: sexual, familial and spiritual, with elegance and aplomb."

—Carole Maso, author of *Mother & Child*

"Short stories that frequently touch on endings—of love, relationship bonds, even life itself—link back to one another in surprising ways in this collection…The confrontations and losses can be gutting, but the ways they tie to one another create a strengthened bond among the survivors; there's hope amid the ruins created here."

—*Kirkus Reviews*

"An affecting collection…about…the things we do for love."
—*People Magazine*

"Caschetta's prose is simple and evocative—and as she skillfully weaves these individual lives together, she reveals a complex tapestry of human experience."

—*Entertainment Weekly*

"MB Caschetta's brilliant *Pretend I'm Your Friend* is one of the year's finest short story collections."

—*Largehearted Boy*

MIRACLE GIRLS

2015 USA Best Book Award Winner for Literary Fiction

2015 Independent Publishers Book (IPPY) Gold Medal

2015 Spiritual Book Winner at the Paris Book Festival

2015 Spiritual Book Winner at the San Francisco Book Festival

2015 Spiritual Book Winner at the Amsterdam Book Festival

Honorable Mention in Spiritual Fiction at the 2015 Los Angeles Book Festival

Honorable Mention in General Fiction at the 2015 New York Book Festival

An IndeFAB 2015 Book of the Year Award Honorable Mention in the LGBT Book Category

An IndeFAB 2015 Book of the Year Award Nominee in the Religious Book Category

Lambda Literary Award 2014 Lesbian Fiction Category Finalist

"Darkly beautiful, *Girls* examines how forgiveness and wisdom take hold in the most unexpected places."

—*People*

"A mesmerizing first novel."

—*Huffington Post*

"In upstate New York, young girls go missing, nuns are revolting, Nixon is resigning, and young Cee-Cee Bianco has visions of the Virgin Mary in this polished debut novel... Caschetta's first novel is filled with a kind of dark poetry and the menace of ordinary evils."

—*Kirkus Reviews*

"Compulsively readable."

—*Lambda Literary Review*

"A stunning debut novel about an unforgettable dysfunctional family and faith."

—*Largehearted Boy*

"This debut sparkles; *Miracle Girls* is that rarest thing: a literary miracle. MB Caschetta will break your heart and mend it all at once."

—Darin Strauss, author of *Chang and Eng* and *Half a Life*

"It's not every day the Virgin Mary makes an appearance in a novel. And how fitting that MB Caschetta invites her into a story where a grandmother provides safety and thousands of prayers; where law-breaking nuns save desperate girls; where life hurts and is full of grace; a world where miracles happen. MB doesn't flinch from writing painful truths nor does she flinch from lifting her characters up and us along with them. *Miracle Girls* is a wonderful book I will give to friends."

—Beverly Donofrio, author of *Riding in Cars With Boys*, *Looking for Mary*, and *Astonished*

"What MB Caschetta's novel brilliantly proposes is an underground railroad for girls. It feels like one of those girls grew up and wrote *Miracle Girls*. I loved reading it and rooting for CeeCee as she struggles to survive her own family and her saintly little girl voyage with the aid of intergenerational healing, and the vintage magic of radical nuns and priests from a time when they worked for peace and helped the lost girls of the world find home."

—Eileen Myles, author of *Inferno: A Poet's Novel* and *Snowflake*

"A wondrous and exhilarating novel. The Bianco family is unforgettable in all its catastrophic dysfunction but also in the capacity of some of its most broken members to fight their way toward salvation. *Miracle Girls* is an unflinching, fantastical and unexpectedly healing act of the imagination. You won't have read anything quite like it, and you're not likely soon to forget it either."

—Paul Russell, author of *Immaculate Blue* and *The Unreal Life of Sergey Nabokov*

A Cheerleader's Guide to Spiritual Enlightenment

ALSO BY MB CASCHETTA

Pretend I'm Your Friend

Miracle Girls

Lucy on the West Coast

A CHEERLEADER'S GUIDE TO SPIRITUAL ENLIGHTENMENT

a memoir in essays

MB Caschetta

AUTHOR OF MIRACLE GIRLS

Engine Books
Indianapolis

Engine Books
Indianapolis
enginebooks.org

Copyright © 2022 by MB Caschetta

All rights reserved. No part of this book may be reproduced or transmitted in any form or by any means, electronic or mechanical, including photocopying, recording, or by any storage and retrieval system, without the written permission of the publisher, except where permitted by law.

Every reasonable attempt has been made to identify owners of copyright. Errors or omissions will be corrected in subsequent editions.

Also available in eBook from Engine Books.

10 9 8 7 6 5 4 3 2 1

ISBN: 978-1-938126-77-2

Library of Congress Control Number: 2022947240

For Meryl

"Your life is already artful—waiting, just waiting, for you to make it art."
—*Toni Morrison*

CONTENTS

ESCAPE, FIND PAPER

"I am stronger than I am broken."
—Roxane Gay

ONCE MORE TO THE LAKE HOUSE

LONG ABOUT 1970, MY father purchased hundreds of acres of uncultivated land forty miles north of our home in the suburbs, which pissed my mother off for nearly four decades.

The first drive we take to see his purchase—up through the little rural farm towns once owned by the Seneca and Iroquois—Mom gets in the car but doesn't say a word.

Herding my brothers into the back of his Blazer, Dad pretends not to notice her face.

"I have something to show you!" Dad says. "Something you'll love!"

His adventures are always exciting. Ice skating on dangerous ponds in winter. Hiking unmarked trails in spring. Camping in summer, complete with a fire pit and hot dogs on sticks, baked beans cooked over a flame right in their tin. Mom squashes all plans for sleeping outside—tent or no tent, stars or no stars—but we still get to douse the campfire with dirt in the bright afternoon and wash up in nature using silt from the bottom of a nearby stream. Underwater, our hands look like a school of little white fish, and we marvel at this trick of using dirt to get clean.

This particular Saturday, the trip isn't about us.

Dad whistles and hums to himself the whole way. He doesn't get mad when my brothers start punching each other in the neck at the first gas station, or when we have to pull over, so I can vomit on the side of a twisty road.

As we crest the top of a sharp hill and coast down to the valley, just a few miles from Dad's surprise destination, he bursts out with his secret.

He has a vision, he says, explaining it in great detail, hunting season by hunting season. To me, it sounds like a plan to kill all the animals: birds, fish, turkey, pheasant, deer, and rabbits. But he says he wants to mark hunting trails in the woods so no one will get lost. To chop down trees and make room for a pond stocked with fish, so anyone with a pole can feel like a fisherman. To build a cabin with a massive fireplace and dozens of cots in a big upstairs room where all his buddies can sleep and rise early to the smell of black coffee and greased rifles.

In the kitchen, he'll be the only chef.

He'll make venison chili with beer for his guests, *pasta e fagioli*, and spaghetti sauce with oregano, the way spaghetti sauce is meant to be made. Mom—who makes hers with paprika—snorts but doesn't take the bait.

When the car rolls to a stop, I step onto motionless land and find the horizon. When my sneakers are solidly on the ground, the somersaults in my stomach come to a halt. I stand next to Dad as he stretches his long limbs on the muddy road and takes in a deep drag of the fresh air. He looks around with wonder. "This is it!" My mother doesn't budge from the front seat, but my brothers scramble out to get a better look at the thick woods on either side of a little dirt road.

"*This* is it?" my oldest brother says—the favorite child gets to have an attitude. "*This* is the surprise?"

"It has to be cleared away," Dad says. "But..."

"But...it's just...trees?" a second brother says, more timidly.

Sometimes Dad likes a good argument; other times, he acts like you're an idiot for having an opinion. I hold my breath for a minute to see which way the wind might blow, but he seems entirely unfazed.

"It'll be our retreat," he tells his three sons, "our very own camp."

Here's the thing Dad loves more than sports, more than even football—the great outdoors!—and he's just purchased a big chunk of it for his very own.

Here is nature at its best: unsullied and pure.

"Someday it'll be a nature reserve," Dad says, as we stand with our sneakers sinking into mud. "You'll see!"

The problem is that we already have a family place for outdoor recreation.

My mother's parents, Nonnie and Beepa, own a house on Lake Ontario across from Canada (that better country) where we go to be together as a family on summer weekends. Beepa and some friends in the trade built the house by hand. He'd learned specialty carpentry in Italy making coffins for his dead countrymen in World War I, too young to be a soldier. He also worked all through the Great Depression in America, where he aged out of enlisting to fight in World War II.

The Lake House itself is a fantastic structure.

On the second floor, it has two family-sized bedrooms: one room for Mom and Dad and our family, and one room for my aunt and uncle and their family. On the first floor, there's a tiny bedroom for Nonnie and Beepa, a living room with huge windows facing the water, a screened-in porch for napping, watching the water, and tuning in fuzzy Canadian TV. The kitchen has a long table with chairs enough for all thirteen of us: six grownups, three cousins, three brothers, and me.

I stay out of the way, reading books, climbing trees, making endless pencil sketches on the back of envelopes, shirt cardboard, and notebook paper. Mostly, though, I follow Nonnie around while she snips green beans in the garden, cooks all our meals, makes popcorn at night, and walks under the spindly pines to see her favorite statue of the Holy Mother, where she bows her head as if to stare at the statue's bare feet, adorned in plaster roses.

I help Nonnie pick wild strawberries and wrestle dandelion greens out of the ground. I help her choose the dark eggplants for dinner that never taste bitter. I help her batter and sauté zucchini flowers until they are golden brown. I help her liberate the spiny middles of artichokes with a spoon, debone the fish, skin the rabbits, and stuff the clams. I learn to cook, watching as she transforms a mound of potato dough into a pile of gnocchi with barely a flick of the wrist.

Nonnie's mother died in childbirth when Nonnie was eleven, and she had to quit school to take care of her four siblings plus the motherless newborn. With her Mass cards and devotion to St. Therese, The Little Flower, you get the idea that Nonnie's learned how to love from the experts.

Upstairs in the bathroom, my mom, aunt, and female cousins get together for the usual eyebrow plucking, mustache bleaching, and hair perming, which are necessary acts of maintenance. Mom always dabs some cream bleach on my upper lip, which burns the skin

"Beauty must suffer," she says.

When my baby blonde hair starts to get dark, she puts lemon juice on my head and sits me in the sun. "Someday, when you're older, you can get your nose fixed, too."

I look in the mirror but can't find anything wrong with it.

Though the sun shines endlessly, day after day, at the lakehouse, and the ideal days are passed in childhood reveries, there's a certain amount of torture that comes with being a girl.

My brothers and cousin hide upstairs in dark rooms and pop out of closets or rise eerily from under blankets to scare me. They tell stories about creatures who live on the shore down by the water and little men who sleep in the crawl space. One entire summer they pretend I'm going deaf by dropping words out of the middle of sentences while still moving their lips. They also try to convince me there's been a change in how to count—"Wrong, Tuner: it's twelve, thirteen, umpteen, fourteen!" They urge me to discuss the matter with my teacher in the fall.

If they're really bored, one or the other of them puts on fake glasses and pretends to be a neighbor's kid from down the dirt road with an uncanny resemblance to our family. Inevitably, the new kid stays for dinner.

There are endless losing bets. Someone (usually me or one of my two brothers in the middle) has to kneel and give someone else (usually my oldest brother) fifteen to twenty "Salami-Baloneys." This is a humiliation my oldest brother adapts from a Saturday morning cartoon, in which you get on your knees, bow to the ground and say "salami," then lift your hands to the sky and shout "baloney" for as many times as pleases the winner. It goes without saying, somehow, too, that there is only one winner in our family.

My oldest brother makes up the secret nickname for me, *Tuner*, which breeds endless guessing games about what it means. My other brothers never tire of trying to figure out the puzzle, but the one in charge, the favorite son, simply smiles and shakes his head. He'll never tell. In no time, everyone picks up the moniker, even my father.

Eventually, the adults get wise to the uneven odds of me versus four nearly adolescent boys. My uncle volunteers to sleep out on the screened-in porch, so that my mother and aunt can reassign the upstairs bedrooms by gender: boys in one room; girls in the other. It feels safe to sleep on a cot surrounded by my two female cousins, my mom and aunt, protected somehow by the sheer number of them. Auntie is much tougher than Mom, and keener on keeping an eye on the boys. If they get out of line, she threatens to knock their heads together. But compared to Dad, the meanest disciplinarian of all, her threats feel empty, almost comical.

When Dad's around, there are limits.

If we get rambunctious, he shouts us down. If someone starts a fight, his glare can stop a kid mid-punch, mid-hair-pull. If one of us gets whiny, sassy, or starts to cry for no good reason, Dad blows his stack, and we all shut up. He employs the cold shoulder to chilling effect, lavishing attention on everyone else around to make it sting all the more.

For the crime of getting on his nerves and being generally shrill or giggly, I'm especially singled out. Dad has a critical eye for my stooped shoulders, horsey guffaw, lack of common sense, and barrage of dumb questions. Sometimes he stares at me until I look his way and see him press his lips together, a reminder to hide my teeth. My mouth is a mess from tripping over the dog's leash in my aunt's garage years before. Almost immediately, my front teeth turn black and refuse to budge, giving my adult incisors nowhere to grow except straight out from the top of my gums.

"Hold your shoulders back," he demands. "Chew gum with your mouth closed. You don't have to shout, we're all right here."

By the age of five I start offering pencil holders and tie clips from neighborhood tag sales on his birthday, but he always puts them aside and sighs. "When are you going to be sensible?"

I don't know the answer.

Since we don't get an allowance, I start finding little jobs to get money to buy him baseball hats with embroidered logos of his favorite sports teams. Before long, I'm walking dogs, looking after neighborhood houses, gathering people's mail when they go away for the weekend or vacation. My services include childcare, which is by far my most lucrative assignment. As soon as I'm old enough, I get real jobs in grocery stores and restaurants, aiming for financial independence long before any of my brothers do.

Though Dad needs more nature than Lake Ontario can provide, it's perfect for Mom who is not the outdoorsy type. After raising four kids all week, she relaxes over the newspaper, leaving our well-being to other trusted adults—her mother and sister, her two older nieces. The Lake House requires nothing more adventuresome than a walk across the gravel driveway from the car to the house on Friday afternoon and from the house to the car on Sunday evening.

If she spends a few moments outside sunning her legs in the yard, it's a lot.

Is she worried that Dad's new land—which he dubs "the Farm" or "The Camp"—will interfere with our summers at the lake? Or is it just her worst nightmare: an open field with wild animals, black flies, swarms of mosquitoes, and who knows what else?

But, as it turns out, Dad has no such designs on her time and no intention of disrupting her relationship with her family. He very quickly lets it be known that his nature reserve is for men only, hunters and fishers.

As our childhood plays out center stage, Dad begins quietly— tree-by-tree, blueprint-by-blueprint, log-by-log—to realize his dream behind the scenes.

In no time, he starts coming much less often to the Lake House. Dropping by on an occasional Saturday or Sunday, he gets in a rare nap or a cocktail with my uncle. He spends the rest of his time delivering babies, he says, which makes a person wonder how many are waiting in line to be born. Without wanting to, I see them, wet and wiggly, sliding out of a hole between someone's legs and dropping into my father's hands.

Whenever he gets up to leave the dinner table, one of the adults excuses him with deference. "Delivery tonight?"

It's never a complaint, but a point of pride.

Nonnie and Beepa love having a doctor in the family. They have a right. They are the ones who worked extra hours to fund Dad's medical school. His own parents, poor factory workers, pressed him into this work (against his will, he says). They didn't have money for his tuition, books, or living expenses, but Beepa was happy to foot the bill to make our mother happy. In return, Dad prescribes minor medications and gives shots in the kitchen for allergies and diabetes. He also sews up cuts when any of the boys get hurt and prescribes Naproxen when any of the girls have menstrual cramps. It's his unspoken duty to look after the family's medical needs, even though we are a remarkably healthy crew.

Without saying goodbye, Dad pushes back his chair from the table and saunters out the kitchen door. From the window or front stoop in our bare feet and pajamas, we watch him drive up the long gravel path and out to the private road. Listening to crickets, we track the orange glow of his cigarette as it becomes a dot that eventually disappears.

"So long, sucker!" my brothers sometimes shout after he's gone.

He's not the kind of Dad to inspire beautiful memories. He's not even the kind to inspire the majority of his own children to become parents—save for my oldest brother. For the most part, as kids, we're embarrassed when he corrects grocery clerks and car mechanics, even the kids on our block who sometimes mistakenly call him "Mister."

"It's 'Doctor,'" he says, as if some dumb kid's little brother is actually judging him.

Dad comes by his difficult personality honestly. His father was even meaner, and somewhere in the patriarchal lineage, several generations back, according to Dad's own genealogy project, there's a great-great-grandfather known in a village in Italy as *Pasquale the Terrible*. These are men who must struggle with alcohol, hot tempers, and bad moods. Dad is inclined to claim that he's much nicer than any of his ancestors, but I find the claim dubious.

I keep my distance and my teeth hidden until the day I have no choice but to let him heal me.

It's Thanksgiving, 1971. We gather as usual, all thirteen of us, at Nonnie and Beepa's house downtown, where we're not allowed to walk by ourselves to Dominic's store to get milk or the paper anymore because the neighborhood is getting "bad," which we know means black because our parents harbor unexamined racist opinions. We are, however, allowed to climb the cherry tree in the backyard and eat fruit right off its branches.

After we finish the turkey and stuffing, I dive under the table to goof around with one of my cousins, but when I stand back up for pumpkin pie, I accidentally tip boiling-hot coffee over my head.

Dad moves fast to grab me under the arms and rush me to a sink of dirty dishes, where he shoves my head under cold running water. At home, he wraps my head, left eye, and most of my face in bandages like a mummy, which he later learns from a plastic surgeon is the exact wrong thing to do.

I feel woozy when he finally releases me to go down to the basement and find my brothers. They're bent over a race-car track near Dad's wine cellar with its dusty bottles whose labels have our last name on them, with "…& Sons" tacked on. Dad has abandoned his mini winery as he has his wood carving, airplane models, pottery, genealogy, photography, beer brewing, and oil painting.

My brothers—twelve, ten, and six to my five—stop what they're doing and look up at me. I'm dazed on pain pills and packed in gauze. The whole undertaking is held in place by rolls and rolls of bandages taped around my head.

"Does it hurt, Tuner?" my brothers want to know.

It doesn't, I tell them; I can't feel a thing.

Disappointed, they go back to their game.

The next day, an eye doctor—my best friend Gina DeSalvo's father—walks over from Waterway Lane to examine me in our family room. He declares that I'm not blind in the burned eye, a relief for everyone. Mom draws open the heavy orange curtains that match the orange shag rug and snaps off the T.V. I've been watching all morning.

"Even so, it's a pretty severe third-degree burn," Gina's father says.

Mom bursts into tears, worried that I'm going to be horribly disfigured, even uglier than I already am.

"I'm sorry," I say, which only makes her feel worse.

I never once go to a hospital or see another doctor. Instead, my father painstakingly tends to my burns at home. For weeks on end, he lifts me onto the kitchen counter, lathers my seared forehead, face, and scalp with PhisoDerm from a bright-green bottle he's swiped from the hospital supply closet, which surgeons use for "scrubbing-in."

It takes over an hour to scour, rinse, dry, and peel my scorched and puckered flesh.

Day after day, for months, my father methodically removes the dead layers of ruined skin and softly cleanses the entire left side of my face with the soapy cotton balls.

I come to love the bleachy, shoe-polishy smell of his efforts.

We never speak during the procedure, but I know Dad is healing me, which means he cares. I long for these special hours, though they are nothing more important than picking scabs.

"Pizza face," my brothers call me.

Like magic, at last, my eye un-swells and my skin renews with layers of fresh epidermis—if not quite perfect, then at least good enough. By summer, the monstrous size and shape of my face go back to normal.

All that's left are a few scars, which eventually fade.

Soon, the whole ordeal is forgotten except for what remains today: a slight discoloration down the side of my face, a silver dollar scar on my forehead that no one ever seems to notice, and a couple of smooth round hairless patches on my scalp under my side part.

Whenever I need comfort, I touch those weird smooth spots to prove to myself that I've indeed landed on a hostile planet through no fault of my own. I'm an alien, an easily injured girl born into a world made for boys. My father is the only other person in the world who knows this secret truth.

My mother never includes the saga of my burnt face among the well-worn family stories she likes to tell. There's the one about her running up the block to return a plate to a neighbor and leaving me for five minutes with Dad on his Sunday off from rotations at the hospital; on Mom's way back home a couple of minutes later, she finds Dad asleep on the sofa and me toddling down the busy avenue about to step into traffic. Or the one about my getting caught writing on the dining room wall with crayons and offering up my own defense in toddler-jumbled syntax: "I didn't have any paper but!" She also has a certain narrative fondness for her sacrifices in motherhood: the time I fell on my face at my aunt's house, bloodying my mouth and snuffing out my baby teeth; how when she came back to get me, I clung tearfully to my aunt, and called her "Mommy," a knife to my mother's heart that can still make her burst into tears.

These bits of stories are enough for me to carve out a road map for life, to stack up a kind of loose narrative of my own, a simple set of directions:

    1) Escape.

    2) Find paper.

    3) Try not to get your teeth bashed in.

CHEERLEADER

MY BEST CHILDHOOD FRIEND Gina DeSalvo lives on Waterway Lane, a few yards away from the Erie Canal. You can smell the putrid stink from her driveway, which prompts rumors among the older kids about farmers dumping dead cows off the nearby Canal Locks.

It's 1975.

River Death is the name of a filmstrip series we've watched all year long. Even Lake Ontario—gigantic and ocean-like—needs rehabilitation. On the radio, Jimmy Carter announces a scarcity of natural gas, petroleum, and coffee.

Nature is running low this summer.

Worse, Gina's become enchanted with a pair of tough sisters who've moved into the neighborhood because their father is a chemical engineer at Xerox. They're exotic girls with movie star names—Charlene (Charley) and Louise (Lulu). Dark-haired and black-eyed, they are far more refined than we Italian girls. No hairy arms, or eyebrows meeting in the middle, or dark mustaches for them. Someone says they're Jewish; my brothers call them Babes. Older by a few years, Lulu is the summer's chief executive activity organizer, though she's clearly bored by us and by everything.

In Lulu and Charley's carpeted basement, they lie on the couch, flipping through soap operas.

Lulu says, "You be the boy."

I'm the one with three brothers, but, still, it seems supremely unlikely that I'm going to carry off any kind of masculinity. I cross my arms and sulk around the television set.

"Not the kid, stupid, the husband."

More direction soon follows: "Start over: Walk in the room, lie down on top of me, and kiss. Act tall, like you mean it. Now, squint your eyes. That's good. Okay, do it again like it's all your idea."

Kissing her is a disappointment; at thirteen she's still miles away from softness. Lying in a dead man's float on the sofa, she's all elbows and teeth—game over the minute it starts.

The rest of the day we play Ping-Pong, or wistfully walk down to the canal, stagnant now, and not ours—a comment on how much has already been ruined. In the woods, we rally a game of dodge ball with the other neighborhood kids or poke leaves with sticks until it gets late.

"Gotta get home for dinner," I say, checking the watch I got for my birthday.

Charley rolls her eyes. "Just set it back an hour and act like it needs new batteries."

My mother isn't fooled: "I don't like those girls."

But whatever she feels or says doesn't matter because Gina's in their thrall, and I am in Gina's.

One afternoon, Charley and Lulu conduct a mysterious study with their father's *Playboy* magazines. Sensing danger, I drum up countless excuses to leave, but they insist on hauling the magazines out of the bookshelves of his home office.

I've seen naked women before. My father is a big Playboy fan, and my brothers keep a box of them in the bottom cabinet of the bathroom vanity. The stacks seem to grow faster than my mother can throw them away.

I stand frozen, as those sophisticated teens sit plucking out centerfolds like magazine tongues, furious activity all around me.

In minutes, dozens of shiny pages gleam up at me from the shag carpet.

"What's the matter with you?" Gina whispers, yanking my shirt. "Get down here and help."

I have no answer, not a single thought in my head beyond *uh-oh*.

"What is it?" Charley says loudly in my face.

I shift weight from one foot to another, trying to be casual.

Lulu gets to her feet, too. "'What in the hell are you smiling about?"

I try to think. Riveted by the glossy girls with their pages wide open, I manage to say, "I have to go." But it's too late: I've already burst into tears.

"What's her problem?"

"Home," I choke out.

Home is where my oldest brother's college search is making everyone tense. His constant handwashing, moping, and grumbling have even sharpened my parents' dull sense of impending doom. Home is where all three of my brothers are due to arrive, piling out of separate carpools from football practice. In August, they have double sessions. They push into the doorway—sweaty, huge, hungry, and half-dressed because of the heat. My mother meets them in the hallway, forcing them to strip so she can wash their jerseys. On any given day in the summer, I can stand in the driveway counting cleats caked with dirt, like dead animals.

"Out of the way, Tuner," they tell me.

Home is where even nicknames are a secret.

I keep up the sobbing until Lulu storms out of the basement, disgusted.

Gina gathers the magazines back in their stacks, handing them to Charley, who shoves them into the shelves of her father's home office. They lead me to a leather couch and let me lie down.

"They're only magazines."

"Don't be such a baby."

They sit down, staring at walls, growing wiser by the second.

I've noticed before how much smarter they are than me. "Okay, stop crying. We'll go to the canal and throw some stones."

But I seem only to be getting dumber.

Already simple tasks become mind-boggling; days jumble, my brain easing from normal lines of thought.

From the first night my brother comes into my room, I'm a train in danger of derailing.

"Don't bug me," I say, half-asleep, convinced it's a joke.

As I fall back into my pillow, he rolls to a belly drop and slithers out.

Sometimes he speaks. "What time is it?"

"I'm sleeping," I complain.

In daylight, he seems his normal, grunting self, though at times I catch him staring at me, a funny look across his face as if the sun's in his eyes and he can't quite make me out. Seven years younger than he is, I grow whispery and cautious.

In the dark, he sits on the edge of the bed, making it shake in terrible rhythms.

It only gets worse.

"What time is it?" "Did you hear something?" "Is Mom in here?"—His questions invade my dreams. Soon I wake up with bruises, my skin turning colors from his pinching, poking, and prodding.

I ask for a lock on my door.

"Stay out of there," my mother tells him distractedly.

The next night, I awake to find his hands in my pajamas. Mute, I roll to the other side of the bed, get up, and go to find my mother.

She's asleep in the living room, TV blaring. "What is it?"

I make a stab, a semi-accusation, trying to name body parts, but the words are so hard to get out. Somehow, my mother translates enough to act. The next day, she brings him a clock radio, explaining that he only wanders into my room when he doesn't know what time it is. This will fix everything, she says, smiling at me.

"But what if he still comes in my room?" I whisper.

"No," she says brightly. "There's no reason now."

"What about the grandfather clock?" I say.

At the bottom of the stairs in the front hallway, there's a large, loud, full-sized clock, which chimes every fifteen minutes and lets loose a big jangle on the hour. No one in the house can ignore it.

She still smiles at me, so I shift gears. "Can I have a lock for my door?"

"Oh, honey," she says. "What if you got locked in?"

A few days later, she gives me a string of bells to put on my doorknob. "Now if anyone comes in your room," she says, "the bells will wake you up."

What then? I want to know. *What am I supposed to do then?* "A lock would be better," I say.

When Charley, Lulu, and Gina take me behind the woods for a stern talking to, they are really just doing their job to protect the neighborhood that summer. No one under the age of thirteen wants a broken girl hanging around to gum up the fun, to point out the actual dangers of childhood. Our world of games revolves around the premise that kids are tough, indestructible, and above all that adults can't hurt us.

"We know," Lulu says. "We know everything."

I stare at her gleaming black eyes. "How?"

I haven't breathed a word except to my mother who urges forgetting, offers bells, chooses to support the male point-of-view that nothing important has happened.

"We have eyes, dummy," Charley says. "How do you think?"

My former ally, Gina, speaks more tentatively, studying the dark dirt floor under her bright white sneaks. "We've been meeting secretly to talk about it."

"You might as well just get it over with and confess," Lulu says.

I start to stutter.

"She's not special," Charley interrupts. "Why are we wasting our breath?"

Gina tugs my arm. "It's the photographs. They arrived today."

I look at the packages in Charley's arms.

"What were you thinking?" Lulu snorts.

Sweat gathers on my upper lip as Charley pulls out the pictures: "We wrote to handsome TV stars."

Lulu steps in with another set of photographs in her hand: "You wrote to *Policewoman*."

"Can you see their point?" Gina asks. "Sean Cassidy and Parker Stevens, not…"

Charley throws the offending photograph at my feet.

Angie Dickinson smiles up at me, an autograph across her neck. I see what they're saying, sort of, as my life veers away from the brick wall of home life and over the steep cliff of treacherous neighborhood girls.

Lulu continues with evidence. "And you like being the boy when we play house. You just can't wait to kiss me. Do you even know what that's called?"

I do not know the name for playing a boy in her game of House, and I hope she doesn't intend to enlighten me.

"Don't forget the magazines," Charley says. "She loves Dad's nudie magazines."

I look at Gina. "No. I wanted to get away from them."

"Same thing," she says. "What for? They don't bother us."

"You did smile," Gina adds in a low tone.

"You're a weirdo!" Charley shouts. "Abby Normal!"

Her sister agrees. "Queer bait."

The wrong question forms on my lips: "Can you help me?"

Surprised, they think it over carefully, eyeing each other for an answer.

"We'll give you one more chance," Lulu says. "But clean yourself up."

"Either act like us or forget it," Charley adds.

After the sisters march away, Gina looks up at me. "You understand, right? You get it?"

I nod my head, eyes blurred with both worry and relief. "Got it."

"Good."

But I don't go back to Waterway Lane that summer. Instead, I sit on the front porch, waiting for August to end. I read books, all I really need to get by, pacing out the rest of my days with the tranquil turning of pages. Sometimes, my friend Steven comes down the block and hangs out with me. His brothers are friends with my brothers; his father is friends with my father, though his dad strikes me as more genteel than mine, a lawyer with a kind smile.

Steven and I don't talk much. We are both depressed. Mostly, we sit on the porch and look out over the lawn. To my eye, he is tall and handsome, insanely musical. But, at school, they call him *faggot*. Sometimes, we shoot baskets at the top of the driveway in a slow, lazy way to pass the time. Our friendship is based on what we have in common: a place we will both have to leave to become who we are.

At home, his dad shoves his face in the toilet as if to flush the gay out, or to drown him. I won't know this fact for a long time, though. I won't know that our friendship is going to last into adulthood. Nor will I know about the many times he tries to kill himself, until one day, many years into the future, when, finally, he succeeds.

On a hot afternoon that summer, while I'm on the porch alone, still on the lam from the neighborhood girls, a car pulls up and ejects four squat dark forms, all of them resembling one another, and somehow, me.

"Cousins from Ottawa?" my mother says, appearing beside me.

"What are they doing here?"

I carefully fold a page of my book, so I can consider the family stretching their limbs in our driveway. We've barely gotten over the last visiting cousin from Canada, who was on a tour of the United States before going to University. Mom said something was really wrong with the guy, though she didn't elaborate; he had troubles. But she still let him pull me onto his lap in our kitchen while he sipped coffee and nibbled Italian cookies. After seeing the sights, he went back home and hanged himself.

Now, my brothers and father come out to see what's going on.

"*Compare*," says the man in the driveway who is a relative of my mother's father, the son of one of Beepa's sisters in Italy.

Dad steps off the porch and shakes the man's hand.

"Cousin, we need help," he says. "Medical advice."

Smiling briefly at the fat woman and the two girls cowering behind her, Dad shows the man into the house, my brothers fast on his heels. Meanwhile, Mom whisks the woman into the house for coffee, leaving me alone with the two girls.

The older one is tall and pretty.

She sits on my chair arm, scanning the sidewalk. Our neighborhood is suburban, filled with Italian lawyers and Italian doctors, like my father. The guy next door works in the carpet business and is rumored to have ties to the local Mafia. Across the street dwells a university Provost. The houses must look strange to them. I imagine their apartment has a fire escape, like an Italian-Canadian version of *A Tree Grows in Brooklyn*, though I actually have no idea where and how they live.

The older girl braids my hair and talks non-stop.

"My little sister has visions; that's why we're here," she confides. "The Holy Ghost comes at night and stands over her, does things."

The little sister is fuzzy-headed and slow; her eyelids seem barely to separate, as if at any moment she may fall asleep. Searching for just the right English words, she touches her stomach and says, "I have an *angel* in here."

Unexpectedly, the screen door opens, and my father comes out to usher the little girl into his office. Before the porch door snaps closed, the older sister and I get a whiff of coffee and an earful of my mother's voice: "Oh, just a quick examination…"

Nonnie and Beepa arrive with dinner. Beepa carries in several freshly skinned rabbits from the Farmer's market, plus potatoes and string beans from his garden. In Italian, Nonnie talks the cousins into staying for dinner.

At the table, the adults speak in a mixture of Italian and English about priests and doctors and children.

The father of the two girls has caramel-colored skin; his fingers tap nervously, mustache twitching. He never looks anybody in the eye, least of all his daughters.

"May all your sons be doctors!" he tells my father.

"I want to be a doctor," the older sister says.

Her father turns away to light a cigar right there at the table and gives it to my father. The older sister opens her mouth, but her mother reaches across the table and clamps her arm down. The smile on my mother's face fades. All I can do, at this point, is focus on the pile of fragile rabbit bones on my plate. I cling to Nonnie's scent—olive oil and garlic—clocking her swift movements around the kitchen. She stops three times to give me a hug.

That night before bed, I ask my mother.

"*Petit mal* seizures," Mom says. "Your father thinks that's what's wrong with the girl."

"What is it?"

"A kind of epilepsy," she says. "She goes blank and sees things."

"Like the Holy Ghost."

My mother nods and presses her lips together. Without warning, my brain is unplugging again; I feel myself slipping into nothingness. But, even so, I know it's not a religious vision that's bothering that distant relative of mine, not an epileptic seizure. There's someone real who stands over her at night. I can't explain why, but the very thought of her makes me welcome the feeling of my own disappearance.

"What if I become a nun?" I ask my mother, feeling desperate and somehow trapped in my skin. "They have little brides of Christ, don't they?"

"You have to finish school," she says in no uncertain terms. "But what about falling in love and having babies? Don't you want that?"

I shrug. Maybe it's not for me.

"Do you feel called to a religious life?" She looks at me with such intensity and surprise that I know I've stumbled on something powerful, something magical and beyond her control.

"Yes!" I say, though I have no idea what it means.

She searches my face. "Well, who am I to say no if God calls you?"

"I don't know."

And I really don't.

How can I know what I don't understand? A thing that can never be proven or spoken. Maybe it never even happened.

In reality, my mother has no intention of letting me become a nun. Nor will she accept a weirdo for a daughter. No doldrums, no depression, no dreams of joining a convent allowed. As I grow more introverted, hanging out on my own—with books, TV shows, stories, and my own imagination—she tracks me more closely.

Weird habits are discouraged, like chewing food an even number of times on each side of my mouth, or gagging when I brush my teeth. It isn't necessary, she tells me; it doesn't fit in with our way of doing things.

In fact, the family culture revolves around Pop Warner, a football league for kids aged five to sixteen, little boys in padded tights clobbering each other or getting clobbered. Pop Warner is our religion. The organization is regimented, categorized into age and weight by groups named Tiny-Mites, Mitey-Mites, Junior

Pee-Wees, Pee-Wees, Junior Midgets, and Midgets.

Despite the titles, the sport is deadly serious.

Inexplicably, even Mom is agreeable to the game. She stands on the sidelines and screams at her sons, "Get him! Kill him! Get the ball!"

Her primary work, though, is comparing us to all the other football families who fill our social life with picnics, planning meetings, pre-game parties, post-game dinners, fundraisers, and awards ceremonies.

It's no contest, of course. We always win.

My youngest brother, only eleven months older than me, is arguably the most talented player. Lithe and quick, good with his hands, he's a running back, catching passes and high-tailing it into the end-zone. It's a movie-star position, which he carries off with charm.

My middle brother hates football, which calls into question everything we believe. To avoid the awkwardness of having to explain himself, he puts on a helmet, sucks in a mouthguard, and runs out to the field every weekend. During one game, he gets knocked out cold for several minutes. The crowd cheers when he gets up and shakes it off, walking in a crooked line to rest on the bench.

"He's okay," the team doctor announces. "Just got his bell rung!"

The team doctor is our father.

My oldest brother plays center, a position for kids shaped like a refrigerator. Since his job is to knock down anyone trying to tackle the bird-boned quarterback, he lifts weights in the basement until his neck is the size of a tree-trunk.

I steer clear of football, try to ignore it, which makes things awkward for Mom, who has no use for my attitude. I'm her only chance for a future filled with popularity and prom dresses.

From my peripheral vision, I see her watching me, calculating. Then, one day, out of the blue, she presents me with the idea of a single narrow escape.

"I'd rather read books," I say.

She smiles broadly, so sure of herself and, suddenly, of me. "It's been staring us in the face all along! Don't you see?"

At first, I don't see. I don't even look. Her best idea up to this point has been bells when you need a lock. Besides, I barely have enough energy to drag myself from the porch to the kitchen, and back again. Dinner is a particularly exhausting event, with one brother starving himself and the other two choking down bread and butter, so they can all make the weigh-in on Saturday and qualify to play in their age group.

"Tryouts!" she says. "You're the perfect age."

"I'll be younger than everyone."

It doesn't matter, mom says; she's the organizer, after all.

I shake my head and sleepwalk back to find my book. "No, thanks."

"Well, it's your *choice*," she says—but means *funeral*.

Mom can wrangle and finagle and wheedle, even get tricky or devious if she has to. She asks me every day for a week; she pleads, bribes, begs, and cajoles. When the deadline passes, she doubles down, putting the screws to me twice a day at least.

"It's not too la-ate!" This, a common sing-song phrase on her way out the door.

My resolve and apathy are no match for her sandpaper determination, which she works until there's no visible line separating her desires from mine.

"Okay," I say, at last. "You win."

Tryouts are at the high school gym, where she's dragged me for years as her helper. I know the process by heart: you practice a new sideline cheer and a couple of jumps all week until it's time to perform them in front of three judges (other football moms under my mother's sway). Afterward, you await your sentence in a hallway with the other girls while all the moms tally the scores. A list goes up with (or without) your name on it. There are only two options: you are chosen or cut.

Since I've waited all week before giving in, I only have a day to learn the cheer and jumps. My performance is pitiful—weighed down and whispery, a fail, just as I suspected. But Mom never flags. She's patient, confident, and encouraging.

"You'll catch on," she says, with a gleam in her eye, as if I'm already the pretty, popular daughter she craves.

When the official list is posted, my name is penciled in at the bottom next to the word alternate.

With a little rigging, my mother sews a letter on a new sweater and small pleats into a navy-blue skirt. Her makeshift uniform nearly matches those of the legitimate squad members. With that, I'm pushed onto a field, pompoms in hand, bright white Keds tied to my feet. My slightly tight skirt reveals gold pleats upon twirling. Though I'm chubby and obviously a fake, the other girls are kind, smiling encouragement and taking me under their wing.

This is the only solution offered, the only escape I have, so I grab it and hold on for dear life.

In the meantime, Mom is a genius at keeping my depression buried in the back yard. "No time to mope," she says, carting me off to practices, scrimmages, games, competitions, sleepover parties, and beauty sessions. We've moved on to glamorous times now; looking like a winner is essential.

Soon enough, everything my mother dislikes about me disappears under a dirt mound in the backyard, patted into the shape of a little girl who has disappeared. My mother is foolish enough to believe that the dead never come back to haunt the living.

What's left is something brand new, an outer shell and an entity all its own.

I call this new thing "cheerleader."

From now until age eighteen, cheerleader stomps and claps and shouts non-stop for football players, sometimes including brothers. Cheerleader urges all those boys to go and to fight and to win.

It hollers and cheers them all the way to the Pop Warner state championships. It grows taller and thinner, a wide white smile flashing out from under buckteeth-correcting braces. It becomes captain of various squads, Junior Pee-Wees, Pee-Wees, Junior Midgets, and Midgets, moving up to the big time: Junior High School, Junior Varsity, and Varsity squads.

For years, it takes part in human walls, pyramids, and towers.

It does jumps, flips, kicks, and falls.

It sends up a rousing, raspy voice at football, basketball, and soccer games. At half-time, it dances to well-rehearsed synchronized steps and shakes pompoms to the beat of *Another One Bites the Dust* and *Eye of the Tiger*. In lock-step with fifteen other girls, the effect is dazzling.

More maintenance is naturally required. Cheerleader curls its hair, plucks its eyebrows, bleaches its mustache, Nairs its underarms, shaves both legs up past the bikini line, stretches to keep leg muscles warm and supple, watches its figure.

Time passes more quickly in daily cheerleading practice, yearly tryouts, monthly rallies, alternating away-game bus rides with the team, banquets, award ceremonies, State and National competitions, even the cheerleading championships, which yield shiny gold and silver trophies.

It rises earlier and earlier to put on the right hair and face. It cares deeply about everything school-related and gets a boyfriend—every bit of effort, worth it.

As flexible as any gymnast, it's also as light now and agile as a bird.

It bends and bows and folds over itself.

It sinks to the floor gracefully with one leg spread in front and the other in back, astonished at how simple it is to split a girl in half.

A little Vaseline on the teeth, and it's smile, smile, smile. Everything is great, except for the suicide journals.

●

It is years before I understand anything; the meaning, for instance, of my oldest brother's childhood nickname for me according to the cousin who was there when he made it up.

Tuner is for tuna because even five-year-old cunts smell like fish.

The next time my oldest brother comes into my room at night, he's been away at college for three years and has been out drinking.

I sit up immediately.

"Get out!" I say. He does.

I stand on top of pyramids now. My sneakers balance on the shoulders of girls who are strong and determined to win. My new place in the world is on top. My message is triumph.

I am the one who will lead us all to v-i-c-t-o-r-y.

WRITING LIFE

"When my brothers try to draw a circle to exclude me, I shall draw a larger circle to include them. Where they speak out for the privileges of a puny group, I shall shout for the rights of all mankind."
—Pauli Murray

"GOD IS A LESBIAN"

THOUGH MY SECRET BACKUP plan is the convent, I go to Vassar College instead.

The campus is strange and beautiful, the first place I live that feels safe. I barely notice the rich kids standing around in judgment, whom some friends sarcastically call "The BPs" for "Beautiful People." In turn, the BPs look down on us because we're "Pubbies," kids who went to public schools.

Despite the class divide, the place allows me to thrive. I read writers I've never heard of before: Margery Kemp, Christine d'Pizan, Monique Wittig, Luce Irigaray, Helene Cixous, Alice Walker, Toni Morrison, bell hooks. I learn an entirely new vocabulary for myself: feminist, queer, depressed, trauma survivor.

The creative writing program in the English Department at Vassar is run the way graduate school workshops are run and is one of the few top notch programs for undergraduates. I meet all kinds of writers who take the train from New York City and let us in on all the different forms a writer's life can take. I want to be a writer, of course. And when the fantasy of a glamorous life wears off, I find that I still want to write. (Eventually I will come back and teach courses in short story writing, and when a new President tries to kill the program in 2008, I fight like hell to save it.)

I train my writing to be minimal like Amy Hempel, noble like William Trevor, mysterious like Carole Maso, fragile like Brett

Singer, bold like Ellen Currie. It's only when I met Grace Paley, a woman so undeniably singular—her twinkle, her sneakers, the gum in her mouth—that I realize I want to write like me. It happens my sophomore year, in a workshop of my writing.

"Not half-bad, kiddo," Grace Paley tells me after I read my story aloud.

"But I want it to be great," I say, and she smiles as if I've stumbled on the secret to becoming a serious artist.

"That's how it starts," she says.

Someone raises a hand. "How do you know when a story is finished, Ms. Paley?"

She picks up her paperback collection, *Enormous Changes at the Last Minute*, and points to the beginning line of the first story.

"Is this word true?" she asks soberly, and moves her finger to the next word. "What about this one?"

She winks and snaps her gum, finishing the entire first sentence of the book in this measured way.

"And this one? Is this word true?"

I finish college in the late 1980s and move to New York City.

I land a job at a literary agency, answering phones, reading unsolicited manuscripts, and waiting for Alice Munro's stories to arrive by mail from Canada, so I can send them, typed on onion-skin paper, to *The New Yorker*, where they are always accepted for publication. All around me, pretty, blonde colleagues rise to the top, marrying publishing execs and getting their manuscripts into print. A depressed lesbian with writer's block, I don't stand much of a chance. Every work day, I wake up with an overpowering feeling of dread.

The city itself is dying of AIDS. On the street, you can always catch a glimpse of someone gaunt who's been kicked out of restaurants, apartments, or families—eventually, funeral homes. At cocktail parties, friends pass around horror stories like lit cigarettes.

Once, at a roof garden gathering, a famous drunk activist

admonishes me for my naiveté. "Darling, *they* are allowed to die in this country because *they* are *you*."

I quit publishing and find a place in my own community—by then something of a boneyard—and join ACT UP, Queer Nation, the Lesbian Avengers. To make ends meet, I work part-time for an AIDS hotline sponsored by the Fund for Human Dignity, a former branch of the National Gay and Lesbian Taskforce. In the meantime, ACT UP gives me a place to point my burgeoning rage and the kind of brothers I've always wanted—nice gay ones.

Jon is my first and my favorite.

He has luminous eyes, a shine to his skin that, at first, I don't recognize as a fever. He flirts with me: "If I were a lesbian, I'd make you mine!" He wonders aloud how an angel—*me?*—has dropped into his life. Though, I meet him during an ACT UP protest, I get to know him after I take a full-time editorial job at Gay Men's Health Crisis (GMHC), where I give him free access to the supply closet across from my desk. I watch as he stuffs his backpack with rolls of tape, boxes of pens, typing paper for his AIDS alternative treatment advocacy reports, which he delivers to researchers at the NIH. I unlock the medical library and let him have his way with the Xerox machine.

By 1993, people I know are either dying or participating in die-ins.

Jon is a former schoolteacher, a writer, and Risa's closest confidante. Jon and Risa live across the hall from one another in a building on First Avenue and First Street, where they argue and get along like an old Jewish couple. She's a nurse. He's a Radical Faerie, which means he's a member of the mysterious gathering of those who perform spiritual rituals in the woods and on mountains in states I've never been to—Kentucky and Tennessee. He goes away for long weekends, and when I ask what he's been up to, he gives me a devilish grin and says, "Wouldn't you like to know?"

Jon has a message for his friends, people who are protesting and working for a cure. "HIV is a gift!"

No one knows what to say.

At ACT UP protests, he doesn't care about the mean Christians holding signs that say, *AIDS is God's Wrath Against Gays!* And: *Jesus Hates You!* And: *Homos Go to Hell!* He doesn't even wait around like I do for the divine retribution that invariably comes with the arrival of an affinity group called The Church Ladies—a brigade of gay men dressed as conservative suburban women and nuns—who show up not to shout down but to sing out in the face of these hateful counter-protestors. In their floral dresses, wigs, and pumps, or their full black-and-white nun habits, they poke fun at the very idea that God could ever be hateful. Their song is always the same and always sung to the tune of "My Country 'Tis of Thee":

> God is a lesbian
> She is a lesbian
> God is a dyke.
> Send her Victoria
> Mary and Gloria
> She'll roll down on the floor with ya'.
> God is a dyke.

Jon waves at them, his friends, but keeps on marching, shouting, chanting, lying down, and getting arrested with the rest of the protesters. *Act up, fight back, fight AIDS!* Only later does he offer up an opinion on the Church Ladies. "Don't get me wrong; they have their purpose; we all do, and I love them. But what no one else seems to realize is exactly how much those religious miscreants don't matter. God loves queers most of all! We're the chosen people; our suffering is evidence. The more they hate us, the more God protects us."

I struggle to wrap my mind around Jon's radical idea.

I stay at his apartment in the East Village and give him tea and aspirin. We listen to NPR and watch old movies on PBS, *Meet Me in St. Louis* and *The Times of Harvey Milk.* Going to sleep, we hear the pigeons fluttering up and down his air shaft, birds that carry *Cryptococcus neoformans,* the cause of Jon's meningitis. One night, while he sleeps, I write a story, titled "Vanish," which breaks a harrowing 5-year writer's block that's been torturing me since my college graduation. In my story, those filthy omnipresent birds turn into angels that carry Jon away.

Rousing at dawn, he's suddenly lucid and a little bit angry. "You wrote a story about me? Sure you did," he mutters. "Bet I die in the end."

When people come to visit, he shouts at them. "This is not about you!"

He confesses to Risa that he's pretty sure he's communing with God on the roof of their apartment building. "Only he calls it fucking," Risa says soberly. He also starts to liken himself to a Messiah.

"All people with AIDS are Christ," he says. "Do you understand what I'm saying?"

Some think it's just the *Cryptococcal* meningitis talking, but I'm pretty sure Jon's got hold of something real: suffering, sacrifice, crucifixion. He's trying so hard to love and forgive that I think it can't just be the result of a swollen brain.

When he passes away at St. Vincent's Hospital on July 12, 1993, it happens a few moments before his parents touch down at an airport in Queens.

They make it to the hospital just as his body is being prepared to go down to the morgue. Shocked and confused, they are angry that they won't be calling the shots at his funeral. "You could have come to see him anytime," someone says. "He would have told you he wanted a political funeral." We hand them one of Jon's essays titled, "The Metaphysics of AIDS."

We show them what he's written about his final wishes, a shocking statement that seems impossible to enact.

ACT UP has already had political funerals, carrying the dead through the street in protest: *This is what AIDS looks like.* Already dumped ashes on the lawn of the White House in protest of no policies, no funding, no public remarks about the epidemic. But Jon doesn't want an angry funeral, he tells us. What he wants is impossible, a puzzle. His affinity group tries to take it as a mandate, but even they can't figure out what it would look like.

Risa writes a poem about it:

> He said, *When I die, I want you to build a fire in the street.*
> He said, *When I die, I want you to burn my body in the fire.*
> He said, *When I die, I want you to eat my flesh.*

Instead, we carry his body through the streets of Alphabet City to Tompkins Square Park, where unhoused people have built an entire miraculous city of shanties and tents to make this park their home.

I am hollowed out by Jon's dying, afraid to sleep due to nightmares that he is really not dead, that he will come back in ways that terrify me, Lazarus of my dreams.

Though Jon's funeral violates just about every city hygiene law, no one gets arrested. The police standby somberly, as we share a small corner square of benches with the residents of the shanties, who bow their head or look away respectfully.

They listen to our speeches and songs, tributes to Jon, and mourn along with us.

Dave shows up at GMHC, a little bit brittle, with cracked lips, crispy hair, and papery skin. He's a volunteer writer for the treatment newsletter I edit.

"I have no one," he tells me.

Because he lives in my neighborhood, I do what I can, which isn't very much. I walk him to the pizza place for lunch on the weekends, drop off groceries, watch TV, pass the time in conversation.

One Christmas Eve, when I take him for a haircut, his lung

collapses, so I hail a cab and go with him to the hospital. We stumble on the curb at St. Vincent's where the good people of Manhattan lend a hand, retrieve a wheelchair from Emergency, and wish us a Merry Christmas. Dave tells each one of these good Samaritans that they're angels. "Just appearing like that out of nowhere?" he keeps saying as we wait behind a white curtain for someone to come and admit him. "It's a miracle, don't you think?"

I stay with him sometimes at night when he's afraid he might die alone in his sleep. I'm in frequent consultation with the only other person on Dave's care team, a dermatologist friend of his, whom I pass in the hallway on my way out or in.

Dave and I talk about our past lives over games of gin rummy. "Would we have been friends if not for this epidemic?"

"You would have hated me." He laughs. "I hated me."

He remembers playing in the ocean with his sister, singing a little jingle they made up: *Man alive, jump and jive.* Sometimes we say this phrase to each other when things look dire.

One night, he asks me to lie on the bed while he goes to sleep before I leave. He's lonely and scared, he says. He has a new home health aide, a woman paid to sit on the sofa all night in case he needs something. She's young and naïve; she misunderstands the terrible labored sound of Dave's breathing when he lies flat. She gets up and leaves abruptly, reporting back to her agency that Dave and I have had sex in front of her.

We laugh, though it isn't funny.

"Can you not see, Miss Thing?" Dave says, as if to her, when he hears this crazy news. "I'm barely alive!"

"Not to mention that we're both gay," I say. "And I don't mean with each other."

"A pervert's a pervert," he counters. "Hello, homophobia!? Double homophobia!"

Dave's family shows up during his final week, earlier than most families do. They're a sad huddle of three lost souls from New Jersey, Mother-Father-Sister, who thank me repeatedly for taking care of their boy.

On Saturday morning, his mother wakes me up with a phone call. She says I should go over to St. Vincent's if I want to say goodbye because Dave has died the night before.

When I arrive, I go down to an empty room in the basement next to the morgue and sit in a bright orange, plastic chair. The only other thing in the room is Dave's dead body on a stretcher. He's covered to the armpits with a sheet, and his skin seems an odd brown color. I sit for a while, not knowing what to do or say, not feeling a single thing.

This is an era of numbness.

People are still dying, there are marches and protests to attend, institutions to tear down and rebuild. We're barely hanging on.

Finally, two orderlies come and take him away.

Dave's sister calls to ask my permission to bury him in their family plot in New Jersey. Her question sparks a kind of detached anger in me. I have no actual idea what Dave wants done with his body; I barely know him, other than as a dying human being in need of help.

"Sure," I say. "Whatever seems right."

"Thanks," his sister says.

"*Man alive, jump and jive,*" I say, but she has no idea what I'm talking about. "Well, anyway, you certainly don't need my permission."

On their way out of town, the sister presses her business card into my hand and asks me to stay in touch.

Year after year, when she sends Christmas cards, I throw them in the trash. I don't even know why I'm so offended. I'm not her counterpart or her competition; I'm just a person who lives in her brother's old neighborhood.

I knew him all of 10 months. Still, the meanness I feel about his family makes me hate not really them as much as myself.

•

To stave off feeling awful, I start to date a healthcare lobbyist.

Though my friends aren't crazy about my finding love at work—they also aren't too crazy about her—the woman sweeps me off my feet with her intelligence and worldliness. I feel that these are the very things I have been lacking all my life, and find her dazzling. The very sight of her makes me feel suddenly alive.

The lobbyist is ten years older than me, with a career that's already at full throttle. She speaks about power the way most people speak of lunch—with a casual certainty that she will soon be served everything she wants or needs.

She tells me she's worked on getting the Americans with Disabilities Act to include HIV as a condition that carries anti-discrimination protections. She tells me she's practically gotten Bill Clinton elected. For sure, it's her influence that gets him to mention AIDS in his first speech as President-elect, the night he declares victory over George H.W. Bush. She even has a hand, she says, in helping devise a universal healthcare plan that will someday be the law of the land. I have no idea if any of this is true, but I decide to believe her. Why would someone lie about something that can so easily be fact-checked? Besides, she's impressively persuasive, has both an ScD from Johns Hopkins and a sense of adventure that's not limited to the bedroom.

I've never met anyone like her.

She takes me on a four-day trip to Puerto Rico, an island she's frequented during health research projects. One night on our trip, she suggests a walk on the beach. She wants to introduce me to an inordinately expensive bottle of champagne. So, we set off together, the warm ocean on our left, the night sky above. We're about to pop the cork when a man in a black ski mask appears from the street side of the beach.

He points two long kitchen knives at her gut and tells me to get on the ground.

"*El piso*," he says.

She takes his wrists loosely in her hands and tells me not to get on the ground no matter what. The guy seems not to understand, so we talk to him in Spanish and to each other in English.

"Run," she says calmly in a low voice. "Go for help."

I'm not about to leave her, but I'm also not about to get on the ground and get raped.

She keeps trying to orchestrate a plan with me, while the guy is yelling that he's going to stab her if I don't do what he says.

"Everyone, stop talking!" I shout. Surprisingly, they both shut up and look at me. "I'm getting down, see? *El piso*."

As I turn to lie down in the sand, I have a familiar thought: *Not this again. Not ever.* At that moment, I happen to spot the champagne bottle standing in the sand with its bright orange label glowing at me like a beacon. I grab it, pivot to standing, and swing the bottle with a full-force blow that makes direct contact with the man's skull. The thud is surprisingly loud: a grandfather clock striking one.

The swipe knocks him off kilter, and he wobbles for a few seconds.

Reeling with adrenalin, I feel something inside snap and loosen, some ancient rage, or a wave of crazy that I've somehow managed to keep locked away until this very moment. *I'm nearly 25*, I think...not sure where the thought is going.

Enough!

I start swinging the champagne bottle wildly and chasing the rapist down the dark beach. I'm shouting expletives in English and Spanish until I run out of breath.

After losing sight of him, I loop back around like a prize-fighter and find my traveling companion staring at me wide-eyed, mouth ajar.

"You're not supposed to run after him," she says.

"Sorry," I say. "I couldn't help myself."

"You could have gotten me killed!" she says and lifts her shirt to show a tiny hyphen-sized cut on her abdomen.

"A scrape or a rape?" I say, intrigued that she's actually angry at *me*. The energy surging through my body is still at a high electric wattage. "What should I have done?"

I can't help but feel triumphant, a person who fends off rapists.

Her cut is covered by a Band-Aid. We haven't even lost the champagne! But my initial glee does not last. Soon, something else takes over, the grown-up version of the damaged kid my mother tried to bury in the backyard so long ago. For many months, even long after this woman and I part ways, I have huge startle reactions, difficulty eating, panic attacks, and find myself falling down that old deep hole, depression.

That night in Puerto Rico, after the police have come and gone, admonishing us for being out alone at night, two women together, on a stretch of beach in a sketchy neighborhood, she apologizes.

"I guess I should have mentioned that our hotel is across from the projects. Everyone says it can be dangerous on the beach after dark."

"I guess so," I say.

Home from the trip, I find a dozen messages flashing on my answering machine, all from my mother with a terrible premonition. "I think something's happened to you! Something bad. Are you in trouble? Please call me."

I call her back and lie. "I'm fine, just back from a weekend away for work."

I never tell her that her feeling is uncanny, that I've barely escaped being raped. But something primal and connected between us snaps back into place.

She calls more often again, suddenly remembering that I'm her daughter, that she knows me well. Maybe it's simply that enough time has passed for her to love me again, even though I refuse to be anything other than the person I am.

A lesbian.

•

Not long after that, the Clinton administration announces a plan to create a national women's health agenda. This is big news. I can't help thinking it provides us a once-in-a-lifetime opportunity.

"We should do something," I tell my activist friends.

"Like what?" they say.

"Like show health policymakers what it's like to be a marginalized woman in a homophobic, racist, classist, misogynist healthcare system." By this, I don't mean us, of course; I mean lesbians with AIDS, the invisible of the invisibles.

Though I'm white and middle-class in a sophisticated urban area, I've had my own run in with the problem. After a brief accident that lands me and a short-term girlfriend in the emergency room at St. Vincent's, two male healthcare providers harass me routinely with phone calls; they want to instruct my girlfriend and me over the phone to give each other enemas. After a while, I report the calls to the Gay and Lesbian Anti-Violence Project and change my phone number.

"It can only be one-hundred times worse for lesbians of color, those who live in poverty, or are seriously ill," I say at our first affinity group meeting. "What kind of living hell must they be going through?"

The obvious thing to do, the activists decide, is to have just such a group of lesbians meet with the head of the Department of Health and Human Services to tell their stories. "We'll give her a taste of what's going on," someone says, and we agree.

Donna Shalala, once an educator in our city, the former President of Hunter College, is passed over to be Clinton's Education Secretary because she's rumored to be a closeted lesbian. More hearsay. Rumor also has it that Clinton appointed her to be the Secretary of Health and Human Services instead.

After formalizing our affinity group, we decide to see if we can get to Shalala directly; meanwhile, because protests are what we do best, we plan one to take place outside the Hubert Humphrey Building where she works.

Every day for weeks, I fax Shalala and include different details from the lives of the lesbians who want to go to Washington to tell their stories. All of them have HIV; all have particular complaints about the healthcare system, not to mention ideas about how to fix these problems. I'm pretty clueless about how hard it is to pull off an ACT UP action and find out just how many hours, how much strategizing, and how many meetings in the community with advocates and activists it takes to make things happen. My colleagues, a group of young female activists, follow the sure lead of Alexis Danzig, a seasoned strategist and safety marshal. Together, we start to plan an ACT-UP style protest to remember.

We take road trips to scout out the site.

We make posters and create a media plan.

We seek out HIV-positive lesbians who are known spokeswomen for the cause to help find other women who might be interested. We rally key advocates: Teresa McGovern of the HIV Law Project, Lisa Winters of the Bronx Lesbians United in Sisterhood (BLUeS), Mary Lucey of Women Alive.

The floor of ACT UP is confused by our action.

"Lesbians can't get AIDS," they say from their privileged seats on the frontlines of the gay epidemic. To them transmission is still somehow about identity rather than behaviors, about lifestyle rather than lives. "Sex between women isn't even a risk for transmitting HIV! It's a waste of resources."

"The women in this action are HIV-positive because of what they do to survive," we explain, "not what they do in bed with other women. They're part of this movement because they need treatment just like you do."

Eventually the Lesbian Avengers and Women's Health Action Mobilization take up our cause, and ACT Up concedes to our affinity group and votes in favor of the action.

My faxes to Shalala are relentless, each one a bit more dramatic, a bit better written than the last.

We begin to question if we should scrap the whole thing, when a call comes in from Shalala's office. She'll take a breakfast meeting with us.

"Great," I tell the aide. "We'll bring the donuts!"

The meeting is scheduled for 9 a.m. on the same Friday that launches the LGBTQ March on Washington, a perfect dovetailing of events, as far as we're concerned. This means the membership of ACT UP—despite lingering political confusion about lesbians and women—will already be in D.C. and will be more likely to come to our protest.

We take a trip to Riker's to meet with some lesbian inmates who have HIV; they make posters for the protest and write letters for the meeting.

When the day finally arrives, lesbians show up by bus, car, and train. We crowd into the building, ready to take the elevator up when a security guard at the front desk stops us, asking for IDs.

One of the women whispers in my ear, "None of us have any."

I remain calm. "Sir, here's my identification." The advocates attending the meeting offer their IDs too. My colleague, friend, public health researcher, Nancy Warren, furrows her brow and says to me loudly enough for the guard to hear. "Is this a tactic to derail us?"

"Just give me a driver's license for each of you," the guard says. "Everyone in America has a driver's license."

The women circling the guard's station look at me and shake their head.

"Not everyone," I say. "No."

"Social security cards?" he continues. "Work or school IDs? Gym memberships?"

"I don't think you understand the situation here, sir."

He is an African-American gentleman who has little patience for our group. "Well, Miss, no one goes into a federal building without an official recording in an official register book of who they are."

"Sir," I say again perhaps a little loudly. "Please call up to

Dr. Shalala's office and explain the situation. They will make an exception. We are not their usual meeting participants." Starting to sweat, I smile reassuringly at him. I'm afraid we won't get up to the office and imagine the disappointment of the group. "Please, call up and explain. I'm sure you'll see they are expecting us."

For several minutes we stand uncomfortably by as the guard decides what to do. Finally, he picks up the phone and dials. Turning away from us, he whispers something into the phone.

At this very odd moment, an elevator opens—out spills the Treatment Action Group (TAG), the very science nerds who've split off from ACT UP to work with scientists at the National Institutes of Health: They're all white or light skinned fellows, all guys dressed in silk ties, pressed pants, and shiny loafers. Looking right through our rag-tag group, they march by—Peter Staley, Mark Harrington, Spencer Cox, Derek Link—carrying with them all the power that their less fortunate sisters with AIDS do not have.

It's hard not to admire them for improving upon medical science, which has remained pretty much the same since 1747 when British soldiers enrolled in the first scurvy trials. The activist-nerds introduced compassionate use and parallel track trials, which gave earlier access to experimental drugs to people with catastrophic disease. Some people, anyway; them, mostly. It's a little hard not to blame them for keeping scientific access so narrow. They are trying to save their own lives, yes; but there are so many others (unlike them, that is to say: without their privilege) who would have benefited too.

Finally, someone with a government badge shows up and escorts the group of us up the elevator to a large, bright conference room. We plop down a few boxes of donuts in the middle of table and take our seats in formidable, well-designed chairs.

We smile nervously and wait. Donna Shalala herself is a diminutive person with a sympathetic face and a quiet power you feel the moment she enters the room. We sit on different sides of the table: us and them.

"Good morning," she says.

"Thank you for taking this meeting," I say. "Our goal here is to have you listen to these women today so when you create a national women's health policy, you'll be informed about their lives and their experience in the healthcare system."

For the rest of the meeting, the women speak passionately about how they became HIV-infected (drug use, rape, paid sex with men), how long it's taken them to get diagnosed (years), what their initial symptoms were (vaginal thrush, mostly) and what their experience in the healthcare system has been, especially since they were identified as lesbians with AIDS (harrowing).

I'm as moved and humbled as Donna Shalala and her coterie of civil servants seem to be. Some sit at the table with us; many more stand against the wall, seeming to listen carefully and take notes.

After the women speak, their advocates chime in with statistics and facts about HIV/AIDS in women and lesbians. They emphasize the legal and social ramifications of a healthcare system and national clinical trial program that do not adequately address the needs of these women and so many others.

During select pauses in the meeting, we hear the chanting outside. *ACT UP. Fight back, Fight AIDS!* Dr. Shalala stiffens slightly at the commotion, but we all keep the meeting moving. What's happening in the courtyard, I later learn, is that hundreds of activists from all over the country have gathered to raise awareness about healthcare for women and lesbians with AIDS. They shout and stomp and ring bells. A group of guys, the usual suspects, get carried away with the spirit of the moment and climb up a light post to hang a huge ACT UP banner cross the front of the Hubert Humphrey building.

The action gets good media coverage. The photo spread in *Newsweek* even includes several shots of the activists responsible for organizing the protest: Alexis Danzig, Berna Lee, Mary Cotter, Anna Kramarsky, and Andrea Daily. It is a rare acknowledgment of the women who consistently fight to get things done, a marginalized group organizing within a marginalized group. We see it as a win to take a seat at the table, to have our say.

It's hard to know how much of a difference it makes, though. How do you know if anything actually translates into women of color getting a safer journey through the system, or better access to treatment, or more humane care? After the actions are over, the best you can do is hope.

One day, during my last year working as an AIDS medical editor for a newsletter called *Treatment Issues*, I find myself sitting in a dark auditorium, waiting for the world's leading AIDS researcher to deliver his latest data on some new drugs that work in combination to inhibit protease in people with HIV. The audience goes silent as Dr. David Ho approaches the podium. He shows his new data on the so-called drug cocktail, suggesting that soon AIDS will become a manageable disease.

"Like diabetes," he says. "Or hypercholesterolemia."

A murmur rises from the audience.

Someone behind me gasps as it sinks in: he's talking about a future in which people with AIDS will have a real shot at something that has been out of reach: survival. We're smack dab in the middle of an epidemic, a place we've started to believe will never end. Practically everyone is dead or dying.

"This is not a cure, *per se*," Dr. Ho warns. "We're still years away from these treatments becoming widely available."

People around me shake their heads, take furious notes. It's impossible to know what to make of Ho's words.

I cannot bring myself to believe what he's saying. This isn't the first time we've been told about possible cures.

I wonder if crying is an appropriate response.

At the moment I'm too exhausted.

We all are.

BLIND EDGE

IN 1997, I HAVE a new girlfriend who measures the health of our five-year relationship on a scale of physical activity. She calls it athletic compatibility, though I don't play tennis, ski, or do much in the water but float. She used to find my sideline approach to life charmingly feminine, but after five years together, my ratings have fallen. "We're getting boring," she says. "Other couples do things, go places, join teams."

I protest. "We do things. We go to movies, eat dinner."

She stands in the middle of the living room in our Brooklyn apartment, exasperated at the sight of me stretched out on the sofa. "*Do* is an active verb."

She's from Cuba, a tumultuous country of revolution and treachery, where leisure is not an accepted hobby.

"We shop," I say weakly, fingering the pages of yet another story I'm writing. "Isn't that something?"

"I'm not talking about purchases. I'm talking about sweat."

We have other things in common: politics, sad films, Joni Mitchell. Incest. I think we're a good match, but it's difficult to know for sure; sometimes being in a relationship feels like standing in a room with no mirrors. Without other couples to offer up a likeness, interpretation is impossible. Lately, though, I've ventured too far alone into my murky past for my girlfriend's comfort. My ills, she complains, are unspecified. *Childhood*, I remind myself, *memory*.

Weekends are especially tough. After she leaves for tennis practice, I think about the old days, when I ran Prospect Park's three-mile loop and went to the gym both Saturday and Sunday. Now the very act of getting dressed exhausts me.

"What are you looking at?" I ask the cat.

To prove all is not lost, I give myself over to a group of other coupled lesbians who want to drag me around the Long Island Sound with a rope tied to a boat, as I attempt to balance on two skinny fiberglass sticks.

"Isn't this great?" my girlfriend asks. "Water skiing!"

Decked out in Speedos of every color, the two other couples in the boat agree. One pair is made-for-TV—a sitcom producer and her very young soap opera star girlfriend. The second couple is tawny, together for decades, and gold-star lesbians joined at the hip. Both couples nod their perfect hairdos into the wind, squinting bright-eyed against the day.

"The sun! The salt air!" one of them says exultantly.

I open more Dramamine, unclench my teeth, and swallow.

When we hit deep water, one of the gold stars takes her turn at a rope that could, it seems to me, quickly entwine around an engine blade or her neck. Nonetheless, she performs the task without incident on one ski. When it gets around to me, my girlfriend offers advice: "You can't drown with a life vest on, but if you get into trouble, let go of the rope, so you don't get dragged under."

"Thanks," I tell her, before jumping in.

After an unfortunate struggle to position myself in a squat, I hear the directive. "Let her rip." Images of free-floating body parts come to mind.

It's too late. Engine revving, the throttle is punched. I lock my knees, clamp my knuckles, stiffen every muscle, and push against the terrible onrush of burning water. The end result is that I'm standing, surprised to find myself skipping furiously across the waves.

My form, I'm later told, is picture-perfect; apparently, water skiing is the only sport in which the act of locking, clamping, and stiffening spells success. I keep my eyes on the wake, a triangle of ridges that threatens to trip me. When the left wake comes close, I shut my eyes, veering over and back, then I cut viciously to the right.

After three hairpin turns around the sound, I signal to cut the engine. The girls cheer wildly as I sink into salt and seaweed that soothe the ache in my muscles. The gold-star couple shouts over the settling water, "Where did you learn to ride the wake like that?" The young soap opera star, who couldn't get up after several attempts, is astounded: "My God, aren't you happy?" My girlfriend helps me into the boat and lovingly wraps a towel around my shoulders. This is when I realize I'm not staving them off. I'm egging them on.

"This Christmas," someone shouts, "snowboarding in Vermont!"

After shopping at Jefferson Market for supplies, we help the gold-star couple rope a small evergreen tree to the roof of their Explorer, then load Christmas groceries, dinner for eight, into the car, for the six-hour drive to Vermont. The twenty-pound turkey is too big for the cooler, so we swaddle it in ice and a Hefty bag, seat-belting it securely between us like a fifth passenger.

My girlfriend puts her baseball cap on top of the lumpy mound.

"Lesbian turkey," she says.

"Lesbian Christmas," I reply.

In separate cars, somewhere along the interstate, is the rest of our party: the two other couples who have cut short their family visits to meet us by sundown. The producer and her actress girlfriend are driving from Cape Cod. A fourth pair who's been together seven years is driving from a family dinner in Connecticut. They own a construction company called Build Your Dream, and this, along with their house-dog-cozy image leads my girlfriend to call them the American Dream.

Our destination, a rented cottage in East Sandwich, Vermont, is a few minutes from a famous mountain for skiers, though we are not planning to ski; we're planning to strap our feet to colorful plastic planks and send ourselves hurtling down miles of ice.

Snowboarding.

"Gonna catch some Big Air," says one of the gold-star pair. Her partner glares out the side window. The Christmas couples break down this way: one daring to snowboard, one not. The construction company couple, who are not especially athletic, refuses as a unit: "We'll stick to antiquing."

"Most common snowboard injury," I read from a magazine for teenagers. "Broken wrists and knees." This doesn't dissuade my girlfriend, the TV producer, or the more athletic of the gold-star couple. For them, women increasingly concerned about the effects of middle age on creaking bones, the snowboard confirms that anything is possible.

"Not turning forty lying down," the sitcom producer says.

"Turning forty flying down," replies the athletic gold star.

"Right on!" adds my girlfriend, forty-two.

I'm not in it for the thrill, but the bargain. One day of daring on the slopes should earn me several weekends of lounging undisturbed. There's also something else, something harder to pinpoint, perhaps the terror of the experience will jostle free some nugget of memory about my past, so that I can halt the incessant archaeological dig into my childhood. Do I expect to find my missing self on that mountain of ice, frozen in some death-defying act of courage? It's possible I simply have a death wish, of course. Or that my relationship is in serious trouble.

"We're the only couple with both people snowboarding," I tell my girlfriend. "Did you notice? Togetherness! Doesn't it make you happy?"

In some ways a relationship is like childhood: You can't assess the damage until the whole thing is over. And even then, the facts are hazy.

Second most common snowboard injury: broken neck.

•

At first light in East Sandwich, my girlfriend hustles us out into a silent snow-covered morning. The rest of the party, we've learned, has been detained by bad weather, and we don't expect them until late afternoon. Not wanting to waste a precious moment on the slopes, the sportier gold star insists we head out early. Her partner waves a mug of coffee from the doorway: "Good-bye. Don't get killed."

"It's beautiful!" my girlfriend whispers, reading my mind.

"Let's stay home and play in the snow," I say.

The Explorer is already warmed up.

"Nice try," she says, and we're off.

Our first day snowboarding the mountain looks like this:

Fall down. Get up. Fall down. Get up. Fall down. Groan. Get up. Fall down. Knock three people down. Get up. Slip. Bang skull, rattle teeth. Fall down. Get up. Trip. Knock skull, jiggle brain.

Get up. Fall down. Get up. Flip over.

Stare at the sky for a while, notice the clouds. Think about crying.

Get up.

Witness three accidents. Know almost everyone involved.

Fall down. Get up. Stay up three seconds. Yell: "Lookatmelookatmelookatme!" Snowboard into a gully, snowboard into a tree, snowboard into a tall man. Fall down. Decide to roll to the bottom. Consider standing up.

Crawl to the chairlift for trip number two.

At home, there is aspirin. Nearly speechless, we sit quietly by the fire, bruised and battered, waiting for the others to arrive.

"I got the hang of it by the end," says the athletic gold-star lesbian.

My girlfriend gives her the stink eye. "You did not."

Cozy from being home all day, the sedentary gold star opens a bottle of wine. "I'd love to say I told you so. And I did tell you so, not that anyone listens to me. But here's what's true: We're old, and evolution is not on our side."

"It says right here," my girlfriend reads, "that you have to go for three days in a row before you can begin to understand the sport."

"Understand?" says the stay-at-home gold star. "What's to understand about banging the base of your skull against ice?"

"Actually, it's enlightening," I say. "I've always wondered if I'd be happier without a brain."

"Are you?" my girlfriend asks. "Happier without?"

I swallow more Advil instead of answering.

The actress and producer arrive with Thinsulate for everyone. "Anyone need battery-operated hand warmers?" one of them says, hauling out a garbage bag full of scarves, jackets, and mittens. On and off the set, they are prepared with props for any and every situation. "Keep the fingers toasty."

The soap opera starlet smiles at me: "I found spandex head wraps in Costumes today." Newly out, she is thirty-two, beautiful and somewhat embarrassed, as if slightly too shy to speak above a stage whisper. Together, in silence, she and I unload state-of-the-art equipment for sled, ski, and skate, until she can't take it anymore. "I feel like an alien."

I pat her back: "Me too, half the time. It's normal." Being close to a newly out lesbian soap opera star is like having someone stand self-consciously bare-naked before you. I wonder at the wisdom of her being so vulnerable in front of her edgy producer girlfriend.

"Fruitcake and canned pâté for everyone!" announces the producer, arms filled with small tin cans and an enormous basket wrapped in red and green cellophane (clearly a corporate re-gift). She is blonde and efficient, full of energy. The gold-star couple stares at her a moment, until one of them thinks of an answer: "Just what we needed."

For dinner, we eat beans and rice, with pâté spread thickly on baguettes from Jefferson Market. The conversation lingers over the construction company couple, still a no-show. The gold-star couple is particularly annoyed at their absence.

"It's not like it used to be. We were best friends with Pia," they complain . "Now she's swallowed up by that business of theirs."

"They're finally turning a profit," I say. "Be a little patient."

"Patient?" one of gold star scoffs. "She doesn't even return my phone calls!"

"Relationships change," says the producer. "Let it go."

The starlet sighs and opens another can of pâté. "Goose liver," she says with delight, passing it around.

At nine p.m., in the pitch black, headlights slice across the front of the little Vermont house, announcing the long-awaited arrival of the missing couple. "They couldn't just call?" mutter both gold stars, breaking away from the group to storm into the bedroom.

We are silent for a moment, staring at one another until someone gets up and opens the door.

Standing alone in the entranceway with a large Christmas wreath that dwarfs her is one half of our missing couple, Elaine, who looks down past her impeccable clothes from Barney's to her construction boots. She's beautiful; also, wise enough not to risk snowboarding, "Merry Christmas," she says softly.

"Where's your other half?" I ask.

"Pia decided to stay at her mom's an extra night," she says. "She's trying to hit them up for a bigger investment in the business."

I picture her missing partner, her flaming red hair bouncing in curls. If Pia were here, she'd roll her eyes at the gold-star couple and say something smart like "What, did we miss the annual lesbian nativity pageant or something?"

Pia thinks snowboarding is fine for other lesbians: "I only take risks involving the heart."

When the gold-star couple reappears from what seems to be an argument in the bedroom, both of them red-faced and out of sorts, there is an awkward silence.

"What do you mean, Pia's not here?"

The other gold star chimes in: "Where is she? What's going on?"

"Nothing's going on," someone else offers. "She's just working, raising funds."

"She doesn't even get a day off at Christmas?" the gold stars stare accusingly at Elaine, who at last puts down the wreath.

Our second day of snowboarding the mountain is very much like our first, with the fortunate addition of the soap opera starlet, who follows along on actual skis like a guardian angel. She documents our spills, averts excess danger, yells at strangers who get in our way. When we manage to stand upright for longer than a flash, she cheers and takes a picture.

Our sixteen-year-old male instructor, Axe, follows behind, too, until my girlfriend and I find our edges.

"Rad," he says. "I really admire your, like, friction."

We learn to tip and tilt our bodies so that the front edges of our board dig haltingly into the ice as we scrape ourselves part way down the mountain, ending in a 180-degree wipeout.

Confidently, we pick ourselves up, setting our back edges deeper, facing treacherously up the mountain while moving the rest of the way down.

The sitcom producer can be found alternately sprawled across our path, lighting a wet cigarette in a gully, or heading recklessly for a tree. In the chairlift, she complains about her young actress lover: "There's something missing about her, something really missing."

"She's sweet," I say. "Aren't we all missing something?"

"I don't know." She rubs her hip. "Maybe I should break up before the New Year. I've turned her into a nervous wreck with all my complaining."

(In the spring, when everything is bursting and new, the sitcom producer will tell the soap opera star to pack her bags and go away; she'll claim never to have loved her in the first place. "But I have proof of your love," the soap opera star protests dramatically, holding out photographs documenting their active life together. By then, the images appear stilted, like blackmail: two girls surfing, two girls sailing, two girls smiling, smiling, smiling.)

"Are you sure Pia's coming?" asks the skeptical gold star. She and Elaine spend the day antiquing.

"I'm sure."

"She'll probably get here tonight," someone says.

After our second day on the mountain, we sit quietly around the evening fire, comparing bruises and downing aspirin with cups of hot chocolate. The sitcom producer presses her temples. "After a while, you hit your head so many times, you can't remember your name."

"Look, I broke my glasses." My girlfriend holds up a smashed pair of expensive Armani frames.

The athletic gold star raises her mug. "Day after Christmas, we do it again!"

"We'll make it down the mountain standing up if it's the last thing we do!" my girlfriend says.

All eyes turn to me.

Half convinced their courage is contagious, I mumble my response. "I'm in."

"You?" someone says. "You're supposed to be the sane half, remember?"

"It's too late to back out now," I say, studying the couples around me. Learning to snowboard, I decide, is like being in love: you're either invested, or you're not. "Much too late."

Christmas eve, as the self-appointed cook, I begin preparations. This turns out to be difficult after the water pump sparks and shorts out. There is a mad search for the yellow pages, a flurry of phone calls.

"Who's going to answer?" someone says. "It's Christmas Eve!"

Elaine goes for a walk alone to smoke a clove cigarette. The gold-star couple begins to sulk. The dominant half of the made-for-TV couple gives her soap-opera-star girlfriend a verbal working-over for leaving her ski boots at the lodge. I look out the window for Pia, who still hasn't arrived, while my girlfriend anxiously observes the chaos. "In my country," she says, "communism got rid of Christmas. Maybe that was a good thing." Nervously, she stokes the fire so hot that we're forced to open all the windows.

In the kitchen, I stuff the twenty-pound turkey with chestnut dressing, cooked when the water pump was still functioning.

"I thought the idea was to escape our dysfunctional families," I tell my girlfriend after everyone has gone to bed. "Not recreate them here in living color."

"It's just stress." She pats the turkey's pale flesh doubtfully, trying to keep her chin up. "It'll be fine in the morning. You'll see."

They are our friends, I tell myself, our counterparts, all we have in the world. I nod my head and smile. My girlfriend puts her arms carefully around me, smiling weakly and says, "That's the spirit."

We take more Motrin and go to bed.

Christmas morning, the oven door falls off its hinges.

"I got it," someone says. "I'll get my drill," someone else. It is a race to be helpful, a competition, proving that bolting a turkey into the oven is a two-woman job.

"Are you sure Pia's coming?"

"I'm sure."

Elaine and one of the gold stars work quickly and silently.

Later, we open presents and cheerfully watch the movie *Bound*, rating the attractiveness of the protagonists according to our own individual butch/femme leanings.

"I don't know," someone says, expressing a nonconformist opinion. "I like them both."

By afternoon, we unbolt the oven and remove a perfect bird, passing around side dishes cooked in melted snow: candied yams, green beans, whole fresh cranberry sauce, artichokes the way my Nonnie made them, garlic mashed potatoes, and four pumpkin pies baked on an open flame.

As my girlfriend predicted, we are transformed.

"To the Swiss Family Robinson," I say, toasting with expensive champagne.

"We can't toast until everyone's here," says the gold star couple. "Shall we call Pia on the cellular?"

We look at Elaine; she is gripping her glass so tightly it shakes.

"Pia left me," she confesses abruptly. "I didn't go to her family's. I just drove around the mountains."

We stare at the turkey. "What do you mean, *left* you?"

"She woke up on Monday and walked out the door with a backpack. I don't think she's coming back."

We sit around morbidly eyeing the stuffing, witnesses to a crime. I imagine our missing lesbian stumbling blindly onto Tenth Street in Brooklyn, leaving her glasses behind on the bathroom vanity, leaving her lover of seven years, the dog, the business, everything.

"Did she say anything?"

"No." Elaine puts down her glass. "Just that she was unhappy."

"What the hell?" my girlfriend says. "We're *all* unhappy."

Our final day on the mountain, we stop halfheartedly at local thrift shops, buying outfits that make us look like adolescent boys. Eager for details, the stay-at-home gold star remains behind with Elaine, now a broken dream. They promise to meet us in the lodge for a drink later.

My girlfriend and I pay for lessons from a young female instructor, who points out problems, discussing our edges and flaws, the tendency of the body to lean one way or another, until we come to a dialectical understanding of the mountain. By the end of the day, we can drift on the board from toe edge to heel edge in a maneuver known as *Falling Leaf*. Gracefully, we etch our way into the ice, falling first forward, then backward, across the mountain's face. Surprisingly, it is backward I like best, the blind edge, with its strange familiarity of not seeing what lies ahead but falling anyway. The air is soft and sustaining, my muscles suddenly seem strong enough to keep me ever upright.

In the lodge at sundown, we gather for hot chocolate, snowboarders and non-snowboarders alike: "What kind of person would end a seven-year relationship in seven minutes?" Elaine asks. She has suddenly come to feel the full force of her girlfriend's betrayal.

"There's a huge mountain for inner-tubing," someone says gently. "Let's all go for a spin when it gets good and dark. It'll take your mind off things."

All day from the chairlift, I've been watching kids on Coca-Cola inner tubes reel down a second ice-slicked mountain that ends in a smooth curl at the parking lot.

"It looks like you could get going fast enough to fly out over the cars," I say. "You could kill yourself and die lying down."

"More snowboarding?" my girlfriend says, a gleam in her eye.

I'm raw from falling down. "Can't I just rest by the fire?"

Our female snowboard instructor shows up in the lodge wearing brightly colored gear. We wave her over, nudging each other at her tough walk.

"You can't always tell," warns the gold-star couple, who know the area best. "In Vermont, everyone walks like a dyke."

We hold up an extra foam cup of chocolate. "Join us for a drink?"

The instructor is cheerful, if slightly vacant. Skipping from topic to topic, we somehow land on bars. The producer tells us of a TV pilot about a gay dance club, making everyone laugh in the right places.

"Yeah, but I'd be afraid to drink in a gay bar," says our instructor, "AIDS and all."

My girlfriend chokes on her hot dog. Everyone looks up, amazed.

Our instructor defends herself. "It is a homosexual disease, very contagious," she says, "or haven't you heard?"

These are the last few days of 1997, the year Ellen DeGeneres is canceled for kissing a woman on prime-time TV, but it is also nearly 1998, the Year of the Oval Office Blow Job; the sexual politics of the day confuse us. We're also weary from decades of feminism and ACT-ing UP. We have fought for and against everyone imaginable: our parents, the government, sometimes even our brothers as they died by the score.

With nothing left to lose, Elaine is the one who gives our exhaustion a voice: "Oh, go ahead," she says. "Have a drink." With that we stand together, as if on cue, and walk away, leaving our instructor alone and slightly puzzled, steam still lifting off the lip of her hot lesbian cocoa.

After dark, it takes thirty minutes for the rest of the party to convince me to lie down headfirst with my arms and legs dangling over an inner tube of air, in order to go up a mountain on a rope and plunge back down at top speed.

"It won't be bad if we do it together," my girlfriend says.

The sitcom producer proposes the event on a napkin.

"You two hold on to my girlfriend, who will tie her tube to mine. You two can each grab an ankle, and you can coat-tail off of them. We'll go down like this, a huge lesbian starfish."

In the crisp night air, one by one, we are towed up the steep incline on our backs. Watching the flat sky darken Vermont, I think of Titian-haired Pia stumbling blindly away and wonder what you put in a backpack when you are leaving for good. I think of the strange world of people, and our female instructor, afraid of lesbians. I can hear my friends behind me, one by one, being dragged up a mountain: someone is singing, someone is laughing. My girlfriend calls my name. It is remarkable, I consider, that anyone ever loves anyone at all. I wonder what God thinks of all this, if God exists.

Are we His favorite suffering daughters on earth—because we're so lost and confused? Any moment now, we'll look up and ask for help.

At the top, we hook up according to plan, a constellation of seven, linked arm and leg in our separate tubes of torture. With a shove from the spotter, our weight gathers speed beyond legal limits, and we plummet into the dark, eyes wide open.

I'm the only one who screams.

It's funny, at first.

Then I realize it's exactly what I've needed, a moment of terror to help me see what there is to fear. Suddenly, I know I'm screaming for my present, not for my past— for all those who are leaving and those left behind. At top speed from mid-mountain, though, it is difficult to tell which is which.

Our futures stretch out confused, like the jumbled lines of the parking lot. The lesbian dream has crumbled, made-for-TV is a lie, and gold-star misery loves company. To top it off, I've been stuck in the past with a girlfriend who wants to live happily ever after. At the fast approach of the parking lot, I scream even louder until my girlfriend grabs my hand.

"Let them go," she says.

Released from the group, we skid out to a separate lane, aiming precisely for the iciest edge. She smiles at me, nodding as if she won't soon disappear, too. I smile back, and hold on tight, closing my eyes, as if we can fly over every parked car in the state of Vermont and be free.

PHARMACEUTICAL WHORE

THE FIRST WOMAN I ever loved is dying.

We've seen each other rarely over the twenty years since my senior year in college, when we had a two-year affair, though we've kept in touch by phone and letter.

It's 2006, and I've come for an unusual emergency weekend stay, but before I can get my coat off, she has launched herself full force into a dance in the middle of her living room. Feet thumping, legs kicking, jazz hands shimmying. In her mid-fifties, Dianne is a generation older, an esteemed professor of renaissance literature, and my former major advisor, lover, and teaching colleague—in that order.

She's not at all the dancing type.

Having driven across the Mass Pike and down the Taconic to discuss her current situation in person, I hadn't counted on entertainment. Out of the corner of my eye, I see her usually rambunctious border collies yawn and blink. It's worse than it seems; she's been at it for hours.

"All morning long!" Dianne says without a trace of her trademark gloom. "I can't seem to help it!"

It is the song "Diamonds Are a Girl's Best Friend."

She belts the lyrics out Ethel-Merman style, adding a clumsy soft shoe across her threaded Persian rug; then, abruptly, stops dancing, looking out over the carpet's edge, as if suddenly remembering that life used to be reliable with hardwood floors and well-wrought plays by Shakespeare.

Dianne's been adept at reading for meaning all thirty years of her career, and yet the current circumstances stump her.

An embedded tumor the size of a grapefruit is eating through her skin and sending lesions to remote locations in her body. It takes three surgeries to remove the thing from her back. Technically: very late-stage malignant melanoma with metastases to the liver and lung.

"An unexpected response," Dianne chirps after the big finish (*Diamonds! Diamonds!*) "Happiness!"

Because I have access to scientific literature, a privilege available to anyone with interest and a few hundred bucks, I know that the serotonin-reuptake inhibitor Dianne has started as a defense against chemo-induced depression can kick in with a rousing bout of euphoria—and, for those who know the lyrics, *I don't mean rhinestones.*

But to a person facing her own mortality, the chemically induced neuronal impact of a new drug on the brain may very well be a useless scrap of information, not to mention inconclusive— who's to say she might not naturally face cancer with a song in her heart? I've witnessed far stranger responses to death: dying, one friend thought he was the Messiah.

I smile and shrug, hold out my arms, careful to avoid the tender zigzag of stitches down her back. I can't help but think of her scar as a swollen red zipper holding her together. Dianne will whip off her shirt at the drop of a hat to show off the surgeon's handiwork.

At the start of this new millennium, I've learned three things so far: 1) medical facts are cold and unyielding, 2) medicine is a science intentionally designed to leave the patient out of the room, and 3) the language of healthcare still does not adequately account for human emotion or the capacity to face mortality head on. Talking with Dianne specifically about her medical condition, I find myself at a loss. I stutter and pause, saying things that are not entirely true.

Who wants to pop the bubble of hope? And, also, who knows? I once told someone that their best friend with AIDS was as good as dead the very month protease inhibitors became available and saved people; that guy's still alive today.

And yet no matter what Dianne's friends and I have been telling her over the past months about courage and positive thinking, about staying strong, I know that her chances for recovery are next to none. What use is all the information in the world when someone you love is dancing on the edge?

Suddenly barking, Dianne's dogs come to life.

She flings open the door and follows them out into the yard, breaking into the skip of a joyful child. I stand perfectly still inside her house, watching from the window.

There are no words. I'm in the wrong business: medical writing.

This is bound to be the last time I see her.

My career in medical communications is a bit of a lark.

After quitting publishing in 1989, my next full-time administrative position is in the Communication Department at Gay Men's Health Crisis (GMHC), which—with its unabashed name on the door—feels like the gayest place on earth. As I pore over every article I can get my hands on about the mysterious virus, I find a weird affinity for deciphering medical jargon and scientific theories. It never would have otherwise occurred to me to enter the medical world, my dad's world, much less stand outside and criticize it. At GMHC, nothing is exempt from vigorous examination: not science, not medicine, not even the organization itself, which, truth be told, is a bit of a mess.

Sexual acting-out is rampant in the new buildings on 21st Street in Manhattan. It doesn't seem to matter what or where it's pointed, a lesson I learn while fending off a creepy bisexual boss who starts leaving pictures of naked men on my desk to ascertain my level of lesbianism [high] and his chances for having sex with me [low]. Many male staffers want to keep the organization a men's club: it's *their* disease, after all, *their* lives. The general stance toward women is aggressive, "Why help us when it's not your problem?"

The question seems ridiculous. What would they have us do? Stand around and watch?

Some women wonder aloud if our gay brothers would show up for us if the tables were turned; I try to believe they would. And yet, female GMHC employees—even those who rise to the top to become directors—are regularly referred to as "bitches," "fag-hags," and/or "dykes."

I'm undeterred. I've had a lifetime so far learning how to provide support in a less than supportive environment. I've been raised to be a cheerleader, a person who roots for brothers whoever they are and whatever they do. Also, there's a new all-female staff protest group meeting in the basement to figure out what we can do to make our work lives easier and the organization more female-friendly.

For the first few years, clients showing up at GMHC's doors have no need for childcare, gynecological referral, or transportation from the outer boroughs. Once it becomes harder to ignore that AIDS is more than a disease of middle-class white gay men, the organization grows tense, nearly splitting over how to provide proper services to women of color, lesbians, gay men of color, poor people, working-class gays, drug users, and ethnic communities.

Race and gender aren't the organization's only blind spots.

Shortly after GMHC's policy department lobbies to help make HIV/AIDS discrimination illegal, thanks to the Americans with Disabilities Act, my friend Joe Fields is passed up for a promotion in the client services department based on his HIV status. Joe's supervisor tells him the organization can't afford another person with AIDS in a supervisory position; there's no extra staff to cover the time off he might need for doctor's appointments—a now blatantly illegal thing to say to him. To the organization's embarrassment, Joe sues. He settles out of court and eventually retires to South Beach.

At about this time, a female director in the education department offers me a medical editing position. She's been watching my work, she says, and wants me on her staff. Editing is up my alley; words come naturally. Assuming I'll figure out the rest, I jump at the chance to edit the organization's medical newsletter, a virtual survival guide for thousands of people with HIV/AIDS and their physicians. In fact, *Treatment Issues* is the best publication of its kind for coverage of news from medical conferences, experimental treatments, clinical trials, and occasionally anecdotal information. Though dense and not particularly well-written, the informative 12-pages are what we have to teach a generation about its disease. The readership reaches far across the country and deep into the nation's capital, where NIH scientists sit tinkering in their labs.

Nervous and upbeat, I arrive for my first day.

The editorial assistant dismisses my attempt to connect. "There were a lot better people than you for this job."

Eventually, though, the guys in my new department come to see that my grasp of grammar and clear writing is useful to them.

I want to do more than just make their ideas readable, of course.

It's as good a moment as any; things are rapidly changing. Patients, for instance, are suddenly offering more than just their bodies to medical science. ACT UP science nerds are helping scientists to accelerate drug approval, grease the R&D pipeline, and get potentially life-saving treatments into their own bodies more quickly. Activists have forced scientists to offer them a seat at the table, where the goal is to design better trials with parallel tracks. New compassionate-use provisions will keep people on drugs after the studies are over.

It's one of those times in the world when anything seems possible.

No matter how benign or toxic or ludicrous, anything that offers hope is fair game. The trick is to discern reality from fantasy.

In my head, an unhelpful voice reminds me that I'm just a girl—what could I possibly know? But I test out my editorial muscle anyway, attending medical conferences, studying journals on infectious disease, and voicing my opinions. Slowly, I begin to make small changes in the publication. I argue for covering women and AIDS, a topic generally regarded by many in the organization as irrelevant. But soon *Treatment Issues* publishes one of the first review articles covering women's medical conditions and HIV as a meaningful topic in the epidemic. A few years later, my supervisors give over to a complete edition of the newsletter addressing issues facing women with HIV/AIDS.

My colleagues don't know, of course, that I've been dreaming of a literary career all my life, working toward it as if the universe owes me something. Writer's block and the practical realities of activism, caretaking, and paying rent have made my dream grow ever distant.

No matter how low my spirits sink, I have to feed myself. Medical writing seems as good a way as any.

Ten years later though, I have one modest book of stories published by a now defunct LGBTQ press called Alyson Books, and am a freelance medical writer with a rotating cache of clients. When there's time, between deadlines, I work on a novel, a second story collection, and some essays.

And yet, it's hard for me to say precisely how I've arrived at the ridiculous juncture of spending my days writing copy for a global erectile dysfunction account, but here I am, a lesbian with vast scientific knowledge about hard-ons. Mostly, I write charts and slides, papers and posters that sell the messages of a pharmaceutical giant: harder erections can lead to better sex.

My favorite kind of freelance gigs are the ones where all I have to do is write headlines and taglines: *The Low-Dose Kick* for a hormone-replacement-therapy (HRT) after research determines that high-dose HRT can cause heart attacks and strokes in women. *Address Your Vision* for an ophthalmic URL that goes live before the country is ready to buy everything, including glasses and contacts, online (web *address,* get it?). *Once Immunized, Twice Protected* for a Hepatitis A & B combination vaccine. The trick to success is loving word games where surviving disease is like winning a marathon, where experiencing relief from pain is like a day in the park, where taking a preventive therapy is like having a guardian angel. (How exactly it works on the American psyche is above my pay grade, but I marvel at the power these ads appear to wield on patients and providers, alike.)

It's surprisingly lucrative to sit in a roomful of "creatives" for a "brainstorming session," where everyone is "blue-skying it" and "thinking outside the box." Pharma companies hire medical communications agencies who hire advertising copywriters like me to make treatments seem sexy, simple, and lifesaving. The ads are aimed at making prescribers feel like the good guys in the treatment of disease.

And yet, it's often queasy, questionable work.

I've refused unethical tasks twice in a decade of work so far. Once, to write a sales brochure promoting a Lyme Disease vaccine that seemed to infect some of the healthy people in the drug trial, according to a close read of the data. Another time, to "try to hide" serious uterine bleeding in materials promoting a product for postmenopausal women. Shortly after my quitting these slimy gigs, the FDA followed suit, removing the Lyme Disease vaccine from market and slamming a black box bleeding warning on the women's drug to halt its promotion.

My first creative director and mentor in the business is the actual inventor of reflux disorder, an endlessly entertaining fact in the industry. His legendary campaign shows a guy holding his chest and saying, "Oh my GERD," instead of "Oh my God," where the letters for GERD spell out a new disease called "gastrointestinal esophageal reflux disorder." The advertising birth of the disease helps doctors remember the name, prescribe the new GERD drug, and eschew old-fashioned remedies for what used to be known as heartburn. This is a career-defining moment of advertising magic that makes my mentor, Kevin McShane, famous among us. Taking a step back, it can also seem like a dirty trick on the public health system and yet another unholy win for overpriced drugs.

An advertising colleague of mine, a former nurse, confesses that she feels she's made no meaningful contribution whatsoever to society for the 20 years she's worked as a copywriter in the pharmaceutical advertising industry.

At the end of her career, she tells me, she can tally nothing beneficial other than her own personal financial gain.

"That's the seduction for writers like us who need to make a living," she says. "The golden handcuffs of a good salary."

I assure her my reasons are pure; I'm supporting my art, after all. I plan to finish my novel and publish it, another book of short stories, maybe even that elusive unicorn, a book of essays, so I can quit.

"Selling your soul to write a novel?" she says thoughtfully. "I hope it's worth it. I really do."

I assure her that I'll quit as soon as I can make a living as an author.

Unfortunately, that day never arrives.

Dianne meets with the study investigators at the University of Pittsburgh Melanoma Center, who claim that their screening tests are foolproof.

No one has died from their study treatment in years. Interleukin-2, an incredibly harsh drug with a slim response rate (<5%), is being tested in the trial. Having been allergic to all other treatments, Dianne sees it as her only remaining option.

In part, she joins a trial because it's near her sister's place in Pittsburgh, though the decision is not a simple one. Dianne's oncologist in Poughkeepsie predicts that the toxic treatment will kill her because she's overweight, pre-diabetic and has smoked most of her adult life. From her breath, I can tell that she's still sneaking

Marlboro Lights despite her diagnosis. Though her organs are not in optimal shape, she passes the required screening tests, which indicate that her lungs and heart seem strong enough for her to safely participate.

"I don't want to sit around doing nothing," Dianne says. "I'd rather fight."

Leaving her dogs with neighbors, she heads to Pittsburgh for several months of difficult treatment, taking in-patient infusions every other week, and spending her off-weeks recovering at her sister's house.

She seems remarkably upbeat about the whole endeavor, sending regular streams of emails with updates and phoning her friends. During the first week of treatment, her lungs fill up with fluid, but she manages to both recover and stay optimistic about what comes next.

"You call this writing?" the guy on the phone asks me.

I'm on a conference call with two guys from one of the larger New York advertising agencies; I'm working for them on an antidepressant account. One guy is an account executive; the other a creative director.

"I don't think you actually understand the first thing about safety and tolerability," says the creative director, who used to be an editor, and seems to need to prove his authority.

I look around my charming attic home office in Northampton, Massachusetts, where freelancing allows me to settle far from New York City. If there were colleagues with me in my office now (or ever), I'd flash a crazy grin at how ingenious my setup is. Mainly, I work and live here (or at the beach in my partner Meryl's place on the tip of Cape Cod), which lets me do whatever I want, pretty much whenever I want.

I remind myself that most of my clients are pleasant and intelligent—people I genuinely like, who genuinely respect me.

The account executive, still on the phone, brings me out of my reverie. "Do you understand what he's saying, Felicia?"

I'm momentarily confused. "Um…my name isn't Felicia."

There's silence on the line.

Felicia is the Senior Vice President who's hired me for this freelance job. She has degrees in biomedical science and marketing and is by far more intelligent in her drunken sleep than these two guys put together.

Felicia is also someone they seem to resent.

The account executive interrupts, launching into his own interpretation of the data in question. "You need to know quite a few things about science here."

I can certainly tell these guys to go to hell; the thought crosses my mind.

But the pay for this project will buy a new boiler for the house in which my office and life are located, a house I own with Meryl. Besides, the changes they want made on my original manuscript are minimal, easy, and have absolutely nothing to do with my understanding of science, which is, by this point, pretty healthy.

They are merely flexing their muscles to feel better about themselves, their rudeness the exception rather than the rule in the work I do.

Besides all that, I'm a seasoned professional in one of the oldest professions in the world, and tomorrow is my 40th birthday, which means there's still time for me to write and publish something that matters. For a person who sells herself to the highest bidder, I'm still very young. Plus, I can swallow just about anything at this point.

"I'll revise and get the manuscript back to you in a half-hour," I say.

Dianne continues to send out emails with updates about her therapy.

It's only midweek during her break from treatment.

My latest email from her comes with a mystery attached: her

sister's family has dug up a small plastic statue of an unknown saint from the garden. "This is a saintly question I've been meaning to ask you," she writes, "as just about the only person I know who might know the answer."

I shoot back an email with a story about St. Joseph, patron of contractors, houses, and homes. Realtors sometimes encourage homeowners to bury St. Joseph statuettes in their gardens to encourage successful sales.

She never gets my message. She dies in her sleep that night. An unexpected turn of events.

Her sister sends me the autopsy report.

The minute I see the first sentence, I regret opening the envelope. I don't want to know the weight of Dianne's brain removed from her skull, the circumference of her heart, or that her empty chest cavity appeared pink and smooth.

This is science, when I'm looking for something else.

Despite myself, I continue reading: her lungs were clear, no sign of an embolism. No discernible cause of death. According to one of the Pittsburgh study investigators, Dianne's death is a mystery.

The head investigator tells Dianne's sister that Dianne probably died of arrhythmia—an electrical disturbance of the heart that leaves no trace. He's quick to add that arrhythmias can happen without a cause, just one of those things.

I do a quick search for arrhythmia and IL-2 and immediately come up with data that show the two are linked.

Dianne's Poughkeepsie oncologist was right; the treatment killed her.

Now and again, I still look for answers—not usually scientific ones, but something more spiritual—and find only more questions. Can you judge a life according to a person's death? Which is more useful at the loneliest moment, courage or fear, hope or pragmatism? Is acceptance the answer, or is it the willingness to fight? Will I die alone, or will someone be there for me?

Dianne's last day on earth was filled with love: taking her niece shopping, writing emails to friends, talking on the phone. She died privately, just as she had lived—alone in the middle of the night. Not lonely, I like to imagine.

I guess that makes her lucky.

What I know of medicine after all these years adds up to very little. Medicine fails many, helps few, and saves no one from the inevitable. Death comes no matter what. For some, it is a gift.

When medicine works, as it does in some instances, we regard it as a miracle.

I think of my friend, Joe, retired in Florida, sending me cards and calendars he makes with his own vibrantly colored photographs. One day, a volunteer from *God's Love We Deliver* discovers his body. Maybe medical science is the reason for his many good years and also for the way he died, peacefully in his sleep. Or is that a separate miracle? I picture the *God's Love* guy all in white, putting down the breakfast tray he's come to deliver, then calling 911.

I think about the feminist activists Teresa McGovern, Linda Meredith, and Risa Denenberg, who once asked me to write a white paper on cervical cancer and HIV to help get the definition of AIDS changed to include female-specific manifestations of the disease, such as cervical cancer and vaginal thrush, so that hundreds, if not thousands, of women could get diagnosed and treated, could be eligible for entitlements the same as their male counterparts. It's probably the most important writing of my life because, eventually, those fierce women won that fight.

I think of my friend Risa, nurse, medical writer, poet, who to this day believes that ACT UP is what taught our community to be bold and face fears without backing down. Lately she's become a student of theology. After decades of science, she says, "It's time to study something else." By this, she means God.

And all along, I'm still sitting at the keyboard trying to make sense of why we live and how we die, or how we live and why we die. It's a gray area people sometimes fill in with faith, and I am not immune, it seems, after all these years. Maybe I'm merely telling myself stories in order to live, as the great essayist Joan Didion wrote in her remarkable collection *The White Album*, one of Dianne's favorite books.

If the act of showing up counts at all, and I hope it does, then I write what I witness because I'm still here.

For now, anyway.

ANOINTED

"There are only two ways to live your life. One is as though nothing is a miracle. The other is as though everything is a miracle."
—Albert Einstein

FOUR DAYS IN SILENCE
(OR GET THEE TO A NUNNERY)

DAY ONE

I'm on my way to a silent retreat in the foothills of the Berkshire Mountains, my cell phone turned to mute. My journey is initially one of despair. It begins on a hot Thursday afternoon in August 2003 on Cape Cod—the least quiet place on earth. *This is silence,* I think, turning off the car radio and listening to the click and whiz of tourists on bikes, the rhythmic lull of traffic, sound of wind blasting in my ear. I'm slightly uneasy, though I've requested this gift for my 37th birthday—unstructured time at the non-denominational spiritual center, *Genesis,* where my friend Risa goes to finish deadlines and take rousingly inexpensive sabbaticals. For years, she's raved about the library, community garden, and flowering grounds. ("You can lose yourself on those wooded trails," Risa says, though I'm more in the business of finding myself. "The labyrinth!") Whether this is a good idea or not, I'm scheduled to spend the next ninety-six hours in wordless, solo contemplation alongside a group of strangers who will be meditating silently on a retreat of their own.

My other friends think it's weird. "Take a trip," they say. "Go hiking."

I stop at a traffic light, humming to calm myself (not silent, yet), leaving behind in the mob of slow-driving, fudge-eating vacationers, the gift's giver, my partner. She has a low-grade fever of about 101°, not unusual for someone with a mast cell disorder, which also causes flushing, shallow breathing, blood-pressure dips, and—in the extreme, anaphylaxis. Depending on the form, mast cell disorders can progress to something like leukemia, though it seems that hers isn't that kind. All the same, my departure creates a number of complications for someone who is only just recovering from months of being acutely ill.

("Please go," she says. "You need this.")

In my mind's eye, I still see her as she was so recently: blue lips, blue nails, about to pass out in a taxi or ambulance as we ride to the nearest emergency room where they never seem able to figure out what's wrong. We spend a year taking those rides while she wastes away, losing hair by the fistful as it fades from auburn to a weird beige. As close as a person can get to the edge without actually slipping over, she is deathly ill, bewildered by this turn of events, but amazingly undaunted. Finally, she finds a hematologist at New York's famous cancer center, Memorial Sloan Kettering, who's well-versed in diseases matching her symptoms; he is the twenty-third doctor in seven months. "Most rare diseases like mastocytosis can take a long time to diagnose," he says.

When her system finally begins to calm down with an abundance of new therapies, we make our escape from New York. We are not the only ones to leave when the air fills with jet fuselage, burning buildings and bodies, but we go far away, moving to the end of the earth—literally—and nowhere near emergency care, an admittedly risky choice for someone with a dire health condition. With money from her first book, my partner has bought a little apartment in one of the old rooming houses in this sleepy, former Portuguese fishing village on Cape Cod. She is somewhat famous in Provincetown, Massachusetts for her columns and book, her plays. Though I have only ever thought of this as an artist colony and haven for LGBTQ tourists, I leave my Brooklyn apartment and move in with her to make it my home, too. This is a place of transience, where the locals don't bother learning your name until you've been around for years. It's lonely here in the off-season and not lonely enough the rest of the year, but I keep my head down. I'm on a writing grant to finish my novel, and I continue to work remotely for medical communication agencies in Boston and Manhattan.

Between fevers, my partner is also writing: a new play and letters to the FDA's Orphan Drug Department to make the argument that the mast-cell stabilizer she has found at the People with AIDS (PWA) Buyer's Club should become available commercially to all mast cell sufferers. The drug helps people with wasting syndrome gain weight, European weightlifters create muscles, and people like my partner stay alive. Though the drug is commonly prescribed in many other countries, she's told that it isn't profitable enough to be launched in U.S. markets. She also spends hours on the phone and online, helping others with her disease get diagnosed and gain access to other medications. She is no longer emaciated, and her hair is back, save for a stripe clear around the circumference of her head where it lost its vibrant auburn color for a while, before starting to grow normally again.

People who don't know her might never guess she's been sick.

So, the fact that I'm driving four hours away for several days indicates I'm having a crisis of my own. Usually, I can shake anything off. I'm like one of those rhinoceros beetles that survives an earthquake, a falling building, the end of times; I just crawl out, dust off, and keep going. In fact, I've outlasted cataclysms, tragedies, dust-ups, and windstorms—mostly from my childhood. I've limped my way through young adulthood and gotten myself into a good relationship with a real shot at love. I should be able to absorb the aftershocks of a little anaphylaxis and a big terrorist attack at this point, shouldn't I? But, instead, I feel numb and paralyzed, overwhelmed by the sudden meaningless of things.

My work, for instance. It's ridiculous. The less I seem to care, the more praise and pay I get. How could that be when I care so much about my novel, which for the life of me, I cannot figure out how to write? Have I wasted the last eight years of my life writing something that's unsalvageable? Worse yet, as I drive away from my partner, my troubles seem trivial, self-indulgent, and privileged. I'm standing in front of a mirror in a mirror, trying to figure out which self is really me.

To top it all off, I've missed a novel writing workshop with Mary Gordon, having signed up months earlier for it at Castle Hill Center for the Arts in Truro. With my check cashed, I sent in my first twenty-five pages for Gordon's review. I wrote the date in my calendar, otherwise empty. And yet, August 9th came and went without me, as did Mary Gordon's workshop.

A simple mistake, but weirdly devastating. What if Mary Gordon is the exact person sent to save my novel?

The evening of the missed early August workshop, I find myself sitting in a pew at Wellfleet's First Congregationalist Church, waiting to hear her read from her new novel. From the last row, I watch the dark church fill up with her friends and fans. She shows up at the last minute, a small cheerful woman of indeterminate age with a face caught somewhere between Jewish and Irish.

I feel ridiculous.

After the reading, I approach her with a book to sign, announcing myself as the student who never showed up.

She looks at me and says, "Oh, you!"

I open my mouth, but nothing comes out.

Filing the awkward moment, she says, "Loved your work!" she puts her hand over her heart, watching my eyes fill with tears.

Now, heading toward Western Mass, I realize how unlikely it is that Mary Gordon—no matter how sincere, how graceful—can be the savior of my mess. Anyway, as with most famous writers, she's probably flocked daily by lowly petitioners and desperados; what's one more to her?

Mary Gordon, Full of Grace, I say to myself for some reason.

The night of her reading, Gordon misses a party thrown in her honor because her husband spikes a fever of 105. I may have decided to go into silence the instant I learn that she too has a febrile loved one too, or the moment she promises to send an email with her thoughts and suggestions about my book, which I know will never happen. But, in fact, I decided to go into silence long before.

Ontologically speaking, Mary Gordon is just the tip of the iceberg.

I take my time driving through Massachusetts, a state I live in but know so little about. There's the Kennedys, of course. And John Kerry. There are a few whispers in the news about marriage for women like my partner and me. There's the Governor's jaunty name, disturbing conservative affiliation, and negative feelings about same-sex marriage. There's hardly a religious institution in the state that's going to go along with the passage of such state-sanctioned marriages.

Driving along the Mass Pike, I notice that trees aren't exactly green here—not like they are in Upstate New York, where the colors, saturated and verdant, draw you in and pin you down. Even the grass seems undecided, gray-green, brown-green, sometimes silver-green. I thought this dull color was limited to the Cape and its lack of topsoil, but now I see I've been wrong about this, too.

A few hours pass quietly as I drive, and before I know it, I'm pulling into the driveway at Genesis.

An unassuming sign marks the entrance.

The grounds are neatly manicured with flower gardens and vegetable patches. I wonder at how skewed my perspective has become after such a short time living on Cape Cod where the combination of light and sea make an ordinary day breathtaking. The buildings at Genesis are squat and made of brick, a bit prison-like, with one exception: a brick carriage house that looks like a historical holdover from the late 1800s.

The main office buzzes with enthusiastic volunteers who operate the Xerox machine, answer phones, and tinker with computers. After brief introductions, I meet my guide, Patricia, also a volunteer. Her eyes widen when she consults a piece of paper and learns that the retreat center's director, Janice, is going to provide me with spiritual counseling during my stay.

"Wonderful!" Patricia says. Before I can protest my need for such a thing, she assures me it's well worth my time. "You don't know how lucky you are! You got the director; she's practically a saint!"

I'm not sure what to make of this. I say, "Well, great, then!"

We pass through hallways, a cafeteria, a greenhouse with fogged windows, and finally, the women's dorm. The walls are cinderblock and speckled with blue and cream paint. The floors are plastic tile molded to resemble wood. The feeling is institutional—a nursing home or elementary school.

On the second floor where my room is, fabric curtains hanging over all the open doors ripple with ceiling fan breezes. This is a silent retreat's version of privacy, I guess. Patricia tells me that I can attend any group activity but can also spend my time alone if I choose.

"There are only women here this week," she says dropping me at a room with a strange mismatch of plaids and florals, a tiled corner with a sink. "But remember, no talking. Shh!"

When she's gone, I pull out my electric toothbrush and turn it on, cutting through the quiet, then turn it off and look around. *Too loud?* I floss my teeth instead.

I wonder if the women who are here to meditate know about my tagging along on their organized retreat. If they do, I'm probably not the person they're expecting.

How could I be?

I'm not even the person I thought I'd be.

•

My spiritual counselor, Janice, is a sprightly septuagenarian with white hair and dangly earrings. She wears a purple t-shirt, white cotton pedal pushers, and sandals that look like Birkenstocks. Her office is covered with warnings about the cats: *don't let them out, please close the door, keep an eye peeled, beware of escape artists*. A long notice explains that these creatures know how to get into trouble. One of them is already in Janice's office, refusing to get off the chair she offers me.

Janice shrugs and pulls up a rocker, motions for me to sit there instead. "Abby Star is a stubborn one."

She speaks with a thick Massachusetts accent. "Sometimes we aren't fully arrived when we get here *physically*."

"I'm not sure how this works," I say.

She talks about my settling in, unpacking bags, about how we carry invisible baggage around, which we never discuss. We might unpack it, or we might not. She tells me about all the places at Genesis where I can go to keep cool—halls that are air-conditioned, fans that can be turned on, switches not to touch.

So far, spiritual counsel is manageable: *Stay out of the heat.*

We're halfway through our session before she lowers the boom. "What's your relationship with God like?"

Here we go, I think. For me, God is paternal and therefore scary. I'm still afraid of my own father so much that sometimes when I call home, and he answers, I hang up the phone.

"God is everywhere, in everything," Janice is saying, as if pinpointing the very origin of my current emotional paralysis. "If you look, you'll find Him."

"I don't want to," I say.

Janice thinks this over, then switches to a new line of questioning. "How do you pray?"

Out of my mouth floats either a terrible lie or an obscene truth. "Writing is how I pray." I avoid mentioning the times my partner and I have prayed together—at first because we believed she was dying, and then because we knew she wasn't.

When I try to explain that I'm here searching for *something* without knowing why or what, she says, "Ah. You've been pulled here."

She tells me to slow down. "Literally walk more slowly."

By being conscious of each footstep connecting to the earth, she explains, we open ourselves up to getting in touch.

Her eyes seem watchful, a little steely.

I feel a bit disappointed by the simplicity of her advice, and yet it's just about my current speed.

It's a task, my first one, and easy enough.

"Take in everything around you; just notice," Janice says. "I think you'll see that our God is a surprising God."

In the hallway, I happen on a line of smiling women waiting—the meditating strangers, I surmise—so I queue up to join their afternoon session. They seem portly and good-natured, sparkly, with short summer haircuts. They wear comfortable shoes and practical cotton slacks with elastic waistbands.

I follow as they enter a modern room with exposed brick, red oriental rug, and a circle of purple fabric chairs. They leave one empty for me, and we sit together with an air of expectation.

No one says a word.

Then, a man in a Hawaiian shirt and green khakis enters the room, the same one who was manhandling the office computer when I arrived. (IT guy?) Because he has stylishly gelled hair and a graying soul patch, I decide he's the guru. He sits unassumingly and closes his eyes, joining us as we wait.

When Janice enters, we all shift our attention to her.

After a moment, she nods at one of the women in the circle who stands and reads from a piece of paper about Jacob from the Old Testament. Jacob is the one who rests his head on a rock and dreams of a ladder that leads to Heaven. When he wakes up, he anoints the rock with oil and calls the place *Beth El*, or House of God.

Janice hands out strips of computer paper with a single message. "Truly God is in this place, and I didn't know it." She gets the women to repeat the sentence in unison a few times, then instructs each to go to the front of the room and rub an ordinary garden rock with what appears to be olive oil. The point, Janice explains, is to remember the places where God made Himself known to us. I'm distracted by wondering if Risa, a Jew, would classify this experience as non-denominational.

It's possible, I decide. Jacob, after all is the father of the twelve tribes of Israel, represented by his twelve sons. He's mentioned sixteen times in the Quran, and in Eastern Catholic Churches is believed to have made the first prophecy of the Theotokos, or the Virgin Mary, because his ladder, like her womb, unites heaven and earth.

The Hawaiian-shirt guy starts talking, praying, actually, calling out to God. "Oh, Great Father and Mother." He's sad about the war in Iraq, he says in a pained voice, invoking God's peace upon us because it has so far eluded the world.

He digs into a long speech, in which every sentence starts with the words, "Oh, gentle and loving God...."

It suddenly dawns that this isn't meditation; it's a church service of some sort.

I look around and read the walls:

Condemned
First fall
Mother and son
Simon and Veronica
Second fall
The women
Third fall
The stripping and the wailing
Death
Descent
Entombment.

Stations of the cross. Do Protestants have them? Or only Catholics?

The last time I went near anything even remotely Catholic was on Good Friday at least ten years before in the back pews of Manhattan's St. Patrick's Cathedral, making out with a girl whose last name ended in *stein*. Coming up for air, she said to me, "I believe this is the day my people killed your Lord."

In ACT UP, affinity groups regularly protested Church attitudes and policies toward gay people, women, contraception, safer sex, and HIV/AIDS. One group dedicated itself to protesting at St. Pat's during Mass. One Sunday, they got in line during Eucharist and tossed the host on the floor, stomping it in combat boots. This caused a rift within the group. Some felt attacking other people's faith went too far; others found it justified. I was horrified to find myself too shocked to register an opinion on the action.

The meditating women stand now, though I've lost track of why.

They mill around, doling out greetings, giving hugs. They crush me with their formidable embraces, patting my back and practically lifting me off the ground. "Peace be with you, MB," one of them whispers. I notice that each wears a glinting gold band on their ring finger.

Slowly, it dawns on me that these meditators are no ordinary dowdy women on a spiritual quest, but nuns.

Jesus who lovingly presides over them from a discreet cross on the wall, face as sweet as a baby's, is their bridegroom.

Not a Buddha in sight.

The guy in the Hawaiian shirt pulls out two chalices—a priest?

Bewildered and exhausted, I open my hands to accept what's offered, a phony if ever there was one. I'm no Catholic, no worshipper of any kind, not since childhood; nonetheless, I eat and drink so as not to offend.

Besides knowing my name, I wonder if they have any idea who I am, or what they'd do if they found out, but nobody says a word—not to me, or against me.

And so, apparently, here I am. In a Catholic Mass.

With a dozen silent nuns.

At a non-non-denominational spiritual center.

Sisters of Providence founded Genesis at the turn of the previous century. Migrating from Kingston, Ontario, Canada, and settling in Holyoke, Massachusetts, they eventually bought this 20-acre plot of land from a wealthy family and used its 26-room home to house their Novitiate.

In 1932, they started a new mission called the Holy Child.

In 1964, the larger building was torn down, as Vatican II launched a mass exodus from traditional convents such as theirs.

In 1991, the sisters repurposed the campus into a retreat center, most recently hosting contemplative dance workshops and ecological conferences.

I read all this in a pamphlet I find in the hallway outside of the main office.

A convent? I have to laugh.

The night before my departure, Meryl and I saw *The Complete Works of Shakespeare, Abridged*, a meta-comedy by Adam Long, Daniel Singer, and Jess Winfield, at the Payomet Theater in Truro, in which a fight breaks out among the three male actors about how hard it is to play female Ophelia, portrayed by our friend Ben in a wig.

To prove it's actually an easy part that anyone can play, the two other actors in the play choose someone—me, reluctantly—from the audience and divide the theater into the three parts of Ophelia's psyche—ego, id, and superego, giving each section a line to chant. The first group voices Ophelia's ambivalence by repeating the word "maybe," while the second group chants "maybe not" on the off-beat. The third section is given a long line to shout, "My biological clock is running out, and I want to have a teeny-weeny baby, so hurry up, Hamlet, and get me pregnant."

It's supposed to be funny.

As the three groups shout out their lines from the audience, the actors turn to me and say Hamlet's famous line about Ophelia's options, also an insult. Using the audience-generated emotion, I'm supposed to scream at the top of my lungs, which I do. All the (male) actors then bow to me as if my scream is the best they've ever heard, proving that any old schlump can play the hysterics of the (mis)interpreted female dilemma.

"Get thee to a nunnery!"

Shakespeare's choice for Ophelia is a convent or a brothel, a play on the double meaning of "nunnery." Though I longed for a sacred place as a kid, I have managed to avoid both convent and brothel; I became a lesbian instead. As for Ophelia, she takes a different route entirely.

She kills herself.

In the middle of the night, I wake with a sense of impending doom. It's too dark at Genesis, too quiet. I can't seem to shake the idea that awful things have happened here, not just in this building but in my room, the bed next to mine. I turn on the light to assess the situation. This fear can't be literal. All the doors are securely locked, Sister Janice told me; they go so far as to change the code for the doors with each new retreat group.

The thoughts persist, formless, unspeakable. I close my eyes to the young female faces all in a row—distraught, distressed. Their mouths gape open as they moan about incest and rape. I try to shake it off.

When I was a kid, I used to pray for God to enclose my bed in an invisible bubble to keep me safe at night, and suddenly I see myself as that little child, like an ink drawing or cartoon character; I'm inside the bed bubble, pressing my hands and face outward, safe but also trapped. This is how I feel now, or maybe it's how the distraught young women feel. They will not stop moaning. But who are they? Why are they here?

I try to summon the words Janice used during our first meeting. "You'll find we take precautions for security very seriously around here."

I lie back on my cot, sweating, wishing I could call my partner, who's asleep by now. Instead, I formulate the message I want to give the tortured women from my sleep, to give to Ophelia, to all women up against the odds, myself included: *Your life matters.* I try to read a book, remind myself that I can leave any time, in the morning if I want, right now even. But I don't move. Neither can I bring myself to brave the dark hallway to use the bathroom shared with the other retreatants. I struggle for a moment with my sense of decorum, pitting it against my fear, then decide what to do.

Emptying a water bottle into the corner sink, I hold it over a little garbage pail and fill it up with the contents of my bladder.

In the morning, in broad daylight, I will flush it all away.

DAY TWO

At 6:30, I'm up and out for a run.

The morning mist is heavy over the pines and oaks. In this light, the buildings seem less prison-like. The main brick structure reminds me of my mother's parish, with its thin cross scaling the façade, glinting in the rising sun. The buildings connect by walkways, short paths with awnings that offer shade. The greenhouse hallway has a massive stained-glass sign facing out: *Faith, Hope, Charity.*

I run past the wooded "prayer paths" and note the hammocks, chair swings, benches that dot the lawn. I'll be okay as long as I run, as long as I can out-pace my past, which seems to haunt me here. On cue, I stumble across a white, plaster, life-sized statue of a woman. The figure tilts her head down to me, hands at her side, palms toward heaven, feet adorned with roses. Nonnie would love it. Ninety-three, and in a nursing home, she calls this figure *The Mother of My God*. The words ring in my ears bringing a lump to my throat and an unbidden prayer to my mind. "Please take away this anger."

I'm asking Nonnie as much as I am *The Mother of Her God*.

I wonder if I should kneel or something, but the mosquitoes are swarming and mist lifting, which prods me forward to keep me from being swallowed up in the supplication.

I hurry back to the dorm, imagining the women are up praying by this hour, but the building is silent.

After a shower, I revisit the meditation room to confirm that it's actually a chapel with the stations of the cross on the wall. In one corner, there's a *prie-dieu*, for kneeling, a gold cross lockbox set out on a table beside several incense holders drilled into the wall.

When I sit near the apparatus, I hear the words, "*Stand up,*" which I do.

"Hello?" I say. But no one's there.

Then, one of the sisters enters and kneels under baby-face Jesus on the cross. I'm too embarrassed to look around or glimpse her face. Instead, I sneak out of the chapel and find my way back to my room (books spread neatly, ceiling fan churning). I sit to write for a few hours, turning out a kind of record of everything that's happening to me, though I leave out the part about the voice telling me to stand.

I sit for a few minutes, trying to figure it out. The voice was not exactly external; it came to me the way I hear my own thoughts, only it didn't originate with me. In other words, though I heard the voice internally, I wasn't the one telling myself to stand up—it felt sort of like thinking someone else's words—confusing.

I shrug this off and clear my mind by reading *Ulysses*, followed by a few pages of Mary Gordon.

"Blame is useless," she writes, sending me back out into the day for a walk through the Chapel of Pines, a dirt path surrounded by gangly silver trees at the far end of the Genesis campus. "But we love blame because without it we're left with something worse: not knowing why."

At lunch, I sit across from the woman who magically knew my name the day before. Sharing a meal in silence is far more comfortable than I had expected. Her silence flows smoothly, like a peaceful stream. I wonder at her choice to become a servant of God; mustn't it be difficult to get up every day and live one's life by faith alone? So much harder, I imagine, than writing one's life as one goes. At least then there's a record, a narrative, a way to understand. But then again, maybe that's precisely what she would say God does for her, a way of understanding. She never looks up from her peach cobbler, sweet with fruit from the Genesis orchard.

In John L'Heureux's novel, *The Miracle*, the priests all struggle with their faith and I wonder if this woman does with hers. One of the priests in the book, dying, lies in bed, "wondering what all this means to be born and live for a while and then die." As the dying priest sees it, there's nothing profound about life; it's a puzzle. Some people have nice lives, and some get shit and hardship and struggle. What difference does it make, he wonders, except to them? "Later, he thinks about praying, but doesn't know to whom he can pray."

But the dying priest goes on praying anyway.

The sister goes on eating her dessert contemplatively.

And the writer goes on writing.

At 2:15, I meet Janice in her office for our second session.

I study her floral summer dress and matching blue earrings, wondering at her vocation.

"Should I call you something more official?" I ask.

She looks at me amused but doesn't answer.

"*Sister* Janice, maybe?"

"Sure," she says. "Whatever you want."

She doesn't bring up the chapel, or yesterday's Mass, and neither do I.

Instead, she asks how I'm doing with the silence. I tell her there's still a lot of chatter going on in my head. "Oh, and I'm afraid here at night."

She peers at me through steel-rimmed glasses but doesn't seem surprised. Again, she asks how I pray.

I sigh then tell her about a sublet Meryl and I rented in New York on Sixth Avenue and Twelfth Street, a box of an apartment with a Murphy bed. Just as her health began to revive, thanks to some medications, America came crashing down. It was as if our personal despair spilled over into the world. We stood outside the Food Emporium watching metal burn in the near distance, as tiny figures—people—jumped to their deaths. When the second building began to collapse, a man standing next to me dropped to his knees. He crossed himself and sobbed.

"No!" he kept shouting. "No!"

A cloud of white cinder puffed up where the building had once stood, and a woman just up from the subway, powdered white in soot from the fall of the first tower, handed us an empty paper coffee cup with a phone number written on it. "Please call my brother and tell him I'm okay."

People formed a line snaking around St. Vincent's Hospital, two and three times, volunteering to give blood for the survivors. We didn't yet know there wouldn't be any.

"A reason to be angry," says Sister Janice.

"I thought a year in and out of emergency rooms had been the worst, and then that terrible, terrible thing happened right before our eyes. What are we supposed to make of it? I believed in God when I was a kid, but now it seems impossible."

She hands me a tissue. "You're grown up now."

I blow my nose. "Yes."

"An adult relationship with God is very different from the one you had as a child. You've seen things; you understand more; you've changed."

I nod. "But maybe God has changed, too?"

She laughs and shakes her head, then suggests I'm searching too hard.

"You don't have to overachieve divinity," she says. "Just let it happen. Imagine if you were always seeking to figure your partner out, to second guess her, to understand what's going on. You'd forgo the actual experience of relating to her, and that would be a shame."

I ask whether she counsels civilians routinely, or mostly just nuns.

She crinkles her nose. "It's not usually all *Catholic Sisters* here. All kinds of people of all faiths come here."

"They just happen to be here on a special Catholic meditation week?"

Sister Janice nods and comes up with a suggestion, "You're a writer; why not write a letter to God?"

"Oh, I didn't come here for that," I say. "I mean, it's not necessary."

"Maybe not," she says. "But write one anyway."

Sister Janice considers me a moment longer, then tells me a secret. "When we look at ourselves, we often see only our faults. But when God looks at us, God sees our beauty."

She smiles at me.

"Think of that," she says. "Only our beauty."

In the hallway, one of the retreating Sisters tells me that a Celebration of Queenship is about to start, but the term eludes me.

"Go see for yourself," she says.

The room is rearranged into two rows of purple chairs on either side of a round table with a lit pink candle as a makeshift altar.

Sister Janice enters the room and introduces Sharon, a slender woman I saw earlier in the garden wearing shorts and a tank top, unusual dress for this group.

Janice says, "Sharon is going to give a special presentation after we read from *The Book of Ruth*." The women all smile and look at me as if every last one of them is a feminist.

Once at my *alma mater*, I taught Jane Hamilton's *The Book of Ruth* in a modern literature class of first-year college students, many of whom immediately dismissed it as "not real literature" due to the Oprah's Book Club stamp on its cover, which prompted me to give an improvised lecture on the history of book clubs and political movements. I mentioned that Shakespeare brought art to the people by aiming his bawdy humor directly at the folks in the cheap seats, but they only blinked at me like sheep.

You're too young to be literary snobs, I told them.

In the Biblical story at hand, Naomi's husband and two sons die in the famine in Judah. Her surviving daughter-in-law, Ruth, proposes a binding arrangement with Naomi. "Don't ask me to leave you!" she begs Ruth:

> Let me go with you. Wherever you go, I will go; wherever you live, I will live. Your people will be my people, and your God will be my God. Wherever you die, I will die, and that is where I will be buried. May the Lord's worst punishment come upon me if I let anything but death separate me from you.

Together, Naomi and Ruth head out for Bethlehem where the Lord shines down on them, blessing all their people with good crops.

After the reading, there's a moment of reflection. Janice encourages us to think of the words as an application of God's Love. *Wherever you go, I will go; wherever you live, I will live.* I think of my own beloved, sick at home. *Your people will be my people, and your God will be my God. Wherever you die, I will die, and that is where I will be buried.* Closing my eyes, I wonder how this passage could be read as anything but a tribute to lesbian love.

Absorbed in the thought, I almost miss what happens next.

At the back of the room, Sister Janice puts on music, and Sharon begins to dance. By the time I look up, she is heading toward the midpoint of the room, moving abruptly and awkwardly.

I peer around, but no one returns my glances.

A male contralto croons steadily as Sharon spins around the room, wind-milling her arms. For a split second, I'm mortified for her, and, then, something remarkable; I see that the look on her face is pure, unfettered joy, which somehow transforms her performance from unseemly to graceful.

In the same internal voice I heard yesterday, I get a new message: *And rejoice!*

Startled, I push the words aside and watch as Sharon wraps up her dance, no doubt an offering to her God. She looks aglow as if nothing else matters: no bills, no tasks, no relationships, no frustration, no sadness. Just dance. When it's done, she takes her seat and closes her eyes, no sign of pride or pleasure on her face, no need to see what anyone else thinks. Sharon doesn't care about her audience; she hasn't danced for us at all.

In the hallway on the way to dinner, I want to say something to her, though I'm not sure what. Could I write the way she dances—with abandon, without worry, not caring what anyone thinks, a dedication to something divine?

But we are back to observing silence, so I pass by without a word.

DAY THREE

In *The Miracle*, John L'Heureux's protagonist is a struggling priest named Father LeBlanc, who's seen a dead girl come back to life. Witnesses deny the girl was actually dead because the idea of resurrection embarrasses people.

LeBlanc has seen a loving mother pray her child back to life with his own eyes but can't seem to persuade anyone else that a miracle has happened. The following Sunday, he gives a homily about a different miracle, a dead man walking out of the tomb alive, Lazarus. He asks his parishioners to consider how much Jesus loved Lazarus to bring him back from death, to consider that he loves each person the same way.

He loves us back to life when we are dead.

The parishioners remain unmoved, but the priest continues, "On the last day, we will be asked the only question that matters: *Whom have you loved back to life?*" I think about my friend Christopher, hospitalized at the age of thirty-seven for trying to drink himself to death. I had gone to college with him, a bright-eyed, foppish guy, graduating a semester ahead of me and going off to Manhattan to write for a fashion magazine. After my own graduation, I lived a block away from him in the meatpacking district, rooming with one of his best friends, Eric.

At the time, we were young and living in the midst of an epidemic. Eric, Christopher, and I spent those early days together, figuring out how to live as adults, getting to know our neighbors, the transvestite prostitutes on the block, the butchers, and johns from Jersey and Connecticut. Every morning, the cobblestone streets ran with blood as beef carcasses hung swinging on hooks. Most nights, Chris stumbled home at dawn just as the meat packers were arriving and tying on aprons.

A few years before his death, we were with him at St. Vincent's when he tried to dry out and get sober. Together, we waited out the DTs, helped clean him up, walked with him through the street to an anonymous room where the haggard held forth soberly, speaking words of wisdom. *Carry the message, not the alcoholic.* How foolish we must have looked on Perry Street with our handsome young friend strapped to our backs.

The three of us had been through a lot, but never our last day together.

In St. Vincent's that last time, Chris had secretly stopped

taking his seizure medication, his antiretrovirals. He put a pillow over his face to show us how we could help him. Finally, like a drowning man, he pulled himself up and looked around the room.

"Sorry," he whispered.

How we loved him, our dear lost friend. But not enough to bring him back.

Browsing through the Genesis bookstore, I suddenly realize it's my father's birthday.

"Your father's electrical impulses are all off," my mother told me recently over the phone, announcing that lately his heart has been giving him trouble, pumping too slowly. Even now, it's hard to imagine my father— doctor, hunter, lover of gin—confronting his own frailty. It seems impossible he could ever succumb to anything, let alone an organ that symbolizes love. But the minute I heard this news, I knew I had to end our estrangement. My mother said he'd forgotten to take his diuretic after a particularly salty meal and had to call an ambulance, for which he waited, leaning on the mailbox. Even now the image sticks: Man clutching chest, out of breath, carrying his own private ocean to the foot of the driveway.

I select a card at Genesis and put a few dollars in a basket to pay for it. I jot a sentence or two, seal it, stamp it, and leave the little campus to find a post office. Believing we've let bygones be bygones, I'm relieved when I get it in the mail.

At my next spiritual guidance session, Janice gets right down to business. "Can you imagine what God wants for you?"

I stare at her.

She launches into an extended metaphor. "It's like a beautiful tree, growing crooked over time, becoming knotted through the years, sprouting brittle branches, battling infestations and problems with the soil, but it's beautiful to our eye anyway, isn't it? This is how God sees. As with all the magnificent creatures of the world, you were created by God's hand. Can you let yourself be loved as God loves you?"

I close my eyes for a moment.

"You have a very strong desire to connect," Janice says, using my name for the first time. "And you've started with models from your childhood, which is the place we all start, the beginning. But now you're a woman. And, yes, maybe you've had a little root-rot in your time, a few broken branches, and maybe a long time ago you experienced a drought. But now it's time to incorporate this suffering into your relationship with the divine."

I think of Jesus hanging on the cross in the other room, arms tied up above his head to hasten suffocation.

"You know, Jesus loved many women," she says. "Imagine yourself as loved, and loving, just exactly as you are. You were created by the hand of God, and God loves what God creates. Don't you love the characters you write? Aren't they special to you despite their shortcomings?"

I nod. For a moment we are silent.

"Let me read you something," she says, and I imagine her pulling a Bible out of her desk; instead, she reaches for two poems by Mary Oliver.

The Journey

One day you finally knew
what you had to do, and began,
though the voices around you
kept shouting
their bad advice—
though the whole house
began to tremble
and you felt the old tug
at your ankles
"Mend my life!"
each voice cried.

But you didn't stop.
You knew what you had to do,
though the wind pried
with its stiff fingers
at the very foundations—
though their melancholy
was terrible.
It was already late
enough, and a wild night,
and the road full of fallen
branches and stones.
But little by little,
as you left their voices behind,
the stars began to burn
through the sheet of clouds,
and there was a new voice,
which you slowly
recognized as your own,
that kept you company
as you strode deeper and deeper
into the world,
determined to do
the only thing you could do—
determined to save
the only life you could save.

I have not saved my mother from her choices. Or my father from
himself. I have not saved the brother who, closest to me in age, is
still mad that I left without looking back. Or my middle brother,
who thinks my writing ruins the family reputation.

I listen to the next poem, too:

Wild Geese

You do not have to be good.
You do not have to walk on your knees
for a hundred miles through the desert, repenting.
You only have to let the soft animal of your body
love what it loves.
Tell me about despair, yours, and I will tell you mine.
Meanwhile the world goes on.
Meanwhile the sun and the clear pebbles and the rain
are moving across the landscapes,
over the prairies and the deep trees,
the mountain and the rivers.
Meanwhile the wild geese, high in the clean blue air,
Are heading home again.
Whoever you are, no matter how lonely,
the world offers itself to your imagination,
calls to you like the wild geese, harsh and exciting—
over and over announcing your place
in the family of things.

I want to tell her that Mary Oliver is a lesbian who lives in Provincetown, too, who walks her dog on the same beach I walk mine. But, instead, I ponder the poem. *Am* I here at this strange retreat center to find my place in the family of things?

"Yes," Janice says.

After the session, I go to the chapel, thinking about being told to grow up. I'll give Janice this, she's got balls. No one joins me, no circle of meditators, nuns, or priests.

Sitting alone, waiting, another message comes in the manner of the others, simple and surprising: *Woman!*

•

On the table at the entrance of the dining room at lunch, Janice leaves copies of a reading from John 20:11-18 about Mary Magdalene standing outside an empty tomb crying. Before the Sabbath, she watches her friend and teacher being spit on, taunted and ridiculed, strung up, and crucified, treated as a pawn in the politics between Romans and Jews. The next day, when she sees the tomb is empty, she thinks someone has stolen her dead friend's body; maybe they plan to parade his cadaver through the streets, she thinks.

A gardener approaches her then and asks, *Woman, why are you crying?*

She answers: *They have taken my Lord away, and I don't know where they have put him.*

When he uses her name, she recognizes that the gardener is Jesus.

Some translations of the line that follows are, *Don't touch me*, or *Don't hang on me*. In this translation, it's *Don't hold on to me for I have not yet ascended to the Father.*

Go instead to my brothers and tell them.

The first appearance after the resurrection is to a woman.

Out for a long run, I listen to Public Radio Amherst playing a stretch of Mozart.

I think about my Christopher, dead for so many years, and all the others who died of AIDS, about Jesus saying, *Woman!* Maybe I do need to grow up. Maybe it's why I can't stop nursing childhood wounds. Has Nonnie been through this? Was she ever told to grow up? Every time I see her in the nursing home, she seems ever more boiled down to her essence, so grateful for all that she's given, so kind to everyone. She tells all the aides and nurses who care for her that she loves them.

"Do you like it here okay?" I asked her once.

Her response was the same for everything. "Oh, yes, thank you; I'm blessed!"

I sit on the acorns in the front lawn of Genesis under the majestic birch and elm and oak trees, just another of God's creatures, according to Janice, listening to Mozart. I recall a phrase from one of the spiritual guidance sessions: "touching the holy." When I finally ask Janice what she means by it, she says, "Do you ever do something so peaceful that you feel there's something sacred happening?" I tell her about walking on the beach with Lillian Hellman, my partner's goofy standard poodle.

Off in the distance, suddenly, something blue catches my eye.

It seems to be a person standing under an archway of pine. The sun glints and bounces as the breeze rustles the leaves, and I can't quite figure out what I'm seeing. My sunglasses add a layer of color, and the motion of everything shows the figure shimmering. This is the same place, I realize, where yesterday Nonnie's statue stood in greater than life-size dimensions. Since the Catholics implant ideas about saints, matter turned into flesh, and flesh turned into matter at an early age, I am startled and stand up to get a better look. I want to make sure I'm not having a stroke or a mystical vision. It's a reflex any person raised Catholic might have. We were told about St. Lucia, and fourteen-year-old Bernadette Soubirous, of any number of young visionaries, though, surely, by now, I've aged out of this possibility.

According to Nonnie, somewhere in communist Yugoslavia the year I turn fourteen, six children begin having visions and receiving messages daily from Our Lady of Medjugorje, Mother of Peace. Medjugorje is a small town close to the Croatian border, largely untouched by the brutal civil war in Bosnia-Herzegovina in the '90s. Last I heard, some of those children, now adults, still receive messages, which they dutifully pass on to a world that couldn't care less. What must their lives be like? I've seen them on news programs like *20/20*, falling to their knees in sync, looking up in reverence, lips moving in unison, rapture shining from their eyes. After a battery of tests, skeptics have long since given up declaring them frauds. Visionaries are often told that they will suffer on earth for the salvation of souls.

And so, a new thought: *Please don't let that statue have a message for me.*

I close my eyes and see a sweaty savior at my side wearing Nikes, running shorts, and a "Save the Earth" T-shirt. We stretch our hamstrings together until I shake it off and find a place where the sunlight no longer cuts into my sight, where the play of leafy shadow quiets with the ebbing breeze. As June Anderson sings "The Queen of the Night," her voice ringing in my earphones like an other-worldly crystal bell, I see the statue for exactly what it is, white and plaster, still as stone.

A tremendous pine has lowered and parted its sloping branches to create a kind of shelter around the figure. My eyes travel up to be sure that they've simply been cut away by some industrious Sister with a sensibility for divine landscaping, but it actually appears that the branches grow that way.

She stares at me kindly, tilting her head.

I stand a moment longer and touch the statue's flowered feet for Nonnie; unable to think of words that wouldn't seem sentimental and corny, I let this be prayer enough. Once a Catholic, always a Catholic.

I'm slightly embarrassed.

But also, weirdly, not embarrassed at all.

Day Four

Listed on the schedule for nine a.m. on Sunday, my fourth day, is a brief going-away ceremony for the meditating Sisters called *a holy anointing*. Sister Janice leaves a little note on my door inviting me to attend. By the time I arrive, she is standing at the front of the room, saying a few words about how, in ancient times, oil was used to heal and honor. She talks about athletes getting rubbed down before and after events, as if these exhausted Sisters are gearing up to get back out on the field and win, some kind of hardy, holy softball team.

Each retreatant is then asked to go to her spiritual director to be anointed for the trip home. Sister Janice calls each of them by name, which is how I learn that Sister Rose, who knew my name without introduction, is also a spiritual director and permanent resident of Genesis, a Sister of Providence like Janice. As I sit in silence, watching them line up, a new message comes to me: *I have chosen you.*

Sister Janice motions to me and I get up and show her my palms. She dips her finger in a chalice of oil and makes an X on each of my hands. Only later will I realize that she's drawn a cross.

"May the spirit continue to inspire you." she says.

"Thank you," I say.

She winks at me. "May your writing inspire others."

Brunch is an explosion of conversation.

The nuns cheerfully run through the people they have in common: Sister so-and-so in Portland, Maine, and Sister this-and-that in Seattle. A small world.

Dancing Sharon tells me she's from Long Island, where she and her community, the Sisters of Grace, also run a retreat center.

"Is that a thing?" I ask.

She sighs. "It's how some communities stay self-sufficient these days."

Betsy, a young woman trying to finish her PhD dissertation, is a non-nun add-on like me; I've seen her once or twice in the dining hall. She tells me she's writing about learning problems among women who've been abused. We briefly discuss Judith Herman's heady, classic book, *Trauma and Recovery.* A woman across the table hands me a piece of paper and pen and asks me to write down the title and author. "It saved my life," I tell her. She's already read *The Courage to Heal.*

"The connection between trauma and a temporary or chronic

lack of mental function makes learning hard for chronically traumatized women," she says.

"The brain comes unplugged," I say.

"Exactly!"

A couple of Sisters give me directions to Stanley Park, the wildlife reserve and sacred sanctuary, if I want a truly "divine adventure." On both of my runs to find this much touted park, I've turned back for fear of getting lost.

"It's quite a ways in," they tell me. "Don't give up too soon!"

One, who serves four missions near the border of Massachusetts with women who've experienced violence, advises me to wait until I see a couple strolling into the park. "Let them get ahead a little bit," she says. "Then trail along behind them; it's safer that way."

I ask Sister Sharon if she's been trained as a dancer, and all the nuns at the table chime in about how moved they were when she danced. Sister Sharon ticks off her experience: ballet as a kid, modern dance in college for gym credit, and once, on a whim, a jazz class.

"I just dance for the joy of it," she says. "That was the *Magnificat*, a musical piece, but also a prayer."

"The *Magnificat* is a meeting between Mary and her cousin Elizabeth, when both are pregnant and graced by God."

"Like your name," Sister Rose says, elbowing me. "MB is for Mary Beth, isn't it?"

"You danced, Sister Sharon?!" Betsy cries. "When? Why didn't I know?"

Suddenly, news passes among us that John Geoghan—a Boston priest in jail for sexually abusing generations of young boys and men—has been murdered in prison, strangled to death. At first, I don't know who they're talking about, or why they're so shocked, but a somber discussion quickly catches me up.

They only use his last name. "Goeghan's been murdered."

"Prison is very tough on sexual offenders," someone says.

"Difficult days," someone else adds. "They're afraid to wear their collars in public, you know."

We are silent for a moment. Then the conversation turns to the women's dorm, which is known to be haunted.

"Oh, yes," a sister says in a low breathy voice. "The mission of the Holy Child here was exclusively for pregnant girls. Some must have died here."

"Is that it?" I say. I want to tell them about feeling the presence of all those poor suffering girls keeping me up at night, but I don't.

"Someone on retreat last year nearly hemorrhaged to death and she was in menopause!"

We consider this.

"Terrible what's been done to girls in this culture," a quiet Sister adds.

Outside the windows, a crisp summer day is in motion.

"Are you ready to return?" Sister Janice asks.

"I have one more day," I tell her.

"Well," Sister Janice says, "I wonder what it will bring."

I shrug, relaxed. My hands are anointed with oil, and Sister Janice's God is a God of surprises.

In the meditation room, I see a lone book on the kneeler. It's about Julian of Norwich, the Medieval mystic who once met with the visionary eccentric, Margery Kemp. Both women published writings about their lives, which became the first such works by women in the English language. Having studied *The Book of Margery Kemp* in college, I'm interested in Julian of Norwich, a spiritual counselor and anchoress, who writes, "all that is contrary to peace and love—is in us and not in God." Many of her visions and messages are "formed in her soul," like an inner dialogue, or God speaking to her in her own thoughts. In this way, she receives her most famous message, *All shall be well, and all shall be well, and all manner of things shall be well.*

Sitting in contemplative silence, a final thought comes to me in my own voice; it's slightly different from the others, not quite as startling: *Ten years.*

"Until what?" I ask aloud. But there's no answer.

I experience a new boldness as I run through Stanley Park.

In the distance, geese honk and screech, like a party. On the other side of a covered footbridge, a platoon stands at attention, orange bills pressing to heaven. Startled, I gasp and falter, and a bunch of kids feeding them fall into fits of laughter. I tip my sweaty baseball hat to them and continue on my way, passing other footpaths, waterfalls, a pond, large meadow, and picnic areas.

Finally, I come to a winding path into the woods.

I hesitate momentarily, looking for the sisters' recommended sanctuary. I wait and follow another runner in, but turn back a few minutes later, feeling lost and telling myself I'll come back some other day.

I won't come back, though. My partner's illness stretches out over months and years; my caregiving role ebbs and flows, sometimes flooding our days. When I get home from Genesis, she folds me in her arms and calls me her little nun. Our love is enough to get us through the thick and thin of the hardships we continue to face together.

Nonnie dies peacefully in her sleep three years after my visit to Genesis, but her absence sends me spiraling down. Two years after that, my father's death only makes things worse.

Exactly ten years to the day of my Genesis visit, I publish my novel, *Miracle Girls*, the final manuscript is dated August 22, 2013. The messages I received there ring in my ears for years, but it's a very long time before I put them together as a single statement to carry with me, a reminder of something I knew long ago.

As I'm turning back toward my car, the river magically appears on my right, and I'm suddenly heading toward a sanctuary guarded by the giant trees. The flow of the water twists around and becomes a bowl, a perfectly clear, perfectly bending glass bowl. The sun is streaming down. And though there are many natural perfections as far as I can see, my eye is drawn to something else. In the middle of the opening where the river is shallow, a single slender, sloping tree bends entirely across the river. To its right and left are rows of stronger related species: the bankers and lawyers of trees. Trees that are famous and celebrated, anticipated, reviewed in the *New York Times*.

But the tree I like best looks as if someone has stripped away all its bark, as if lightning has struck it twice. It grows sideways, unlike anything else in this up-growing universe, unique and noteworthy.

I take a deep breath. My life is not at all what I expected.

Beautiful, Sister Janice would say.

THIS COMES NEXT

DON'T GET ME WRONG: Lillian Hellman is no saint.

She eats garbage, knocks down toddlers, and leaves sand in the sheets, though, technically, she's not allowed on the bed. She doesn't always come when called, particularly when she's stealing another dog's ball. Her loyalty is not to me, anyway; she belongs to my partner.

Still, Lilly and I have found a happy rhythm for living here in Provincetown—new to me, old hat to her.

What we do is walk the harbor: she—zipped up tight in her black poodle suit (standard issue), showing signs of her age (more slowly, I think, than my own hair is turning silver); me—dressed for the season in the previous day's sweater.

We pay attention to the tides: moody sea, salty breeze, the ever-rolling sky.

We track the trends.

Monday, dark and choppy.

Tuesday, smooth as glass.

Wednesday, there's a seal, a prehistoric lady taking in the sun who yawns at Lilly's barking. *Stay back*, Lilly seems to warn, running a wide circle.

Thursday, a storm makes the local news, and we turn back regretfully, knowing just the same we've made the right decision.

Friday's all a-glitter.

Saturday—the same.

Sunday, something slimy in her teeth, the shimmery innards of some shelled urchin, which later makes her sick.

We are lowly students of the complex natural world, not as smart as we should be, mouths hanging open, daunted by the journey. *Too hard*, we think some days. *Too long, a little wearing.* Then the sea dries up, becomes the land, and we head out boldly, as if walking on water is what we do best.

"Everything changes," I say, going as far as the low tide allows.

But Lilly is the true master—she chases a feather, paws the waves, sighs, draws a breath—an expert at surrender. She is proof to me that something great and mysterious is at work, which we should be grateful to accept.

One night, something happens, though it's hard to say what.

A synapse misfires.

A disk compresses.

Or maybe a clot gets lodged in the spaghetti veins of her legs. Whatever the cause, the hind two stiffen and refuse to budge.

She crashes to the floor, wakes us from dreams, front-limbs scraping like an old woman who's fallen out of bed. Unexpected.

Lillian Hellman, walker of tides, grows desperate as her namesake. She lies paralyzed, as if drunk, on the peach-painted floor.

Stoic, she doesn't whimper, a better bitch than I am—follower of Zen philosophy—*This is now*, she seems to say. *This is what comes next.*

Her bladder empties, as she trembles and shakes, still managing to wag her tail when we fall to her side.

Legless as a seal, she is gathered up in her mother's arms. (I am not her mother. I am just her walker.)

We stretch her out between us, stiff as *rigor mortis*.

Then, as suddenly as it's spring, she's up again and wagging, stretching those stiff legs back with perfect yoga grace. She's grateful for the comfort.

All we need, she seems to say of our willingness to hold her head, rub her legs, see her through the night. *All we ever need.*

The moment passes, and we climb into bed.

I worry about the future, dream of never giving up.

I'll carry her down the stairs if I have to, out to the street, past the Boatslip and sand. I'll wade with her in my arms, cradled like a baby (not mine, but still), and we'll float if we must, if she cannot walk.

We'll float out to sea.

LOVE AT LAST

"Like air, I'll rise."
—*Maya Angelou*

ITALIAN BRIDE

I'M TWELVE YEARS OLD when my mother starts dragging me to the dark back pews in stone cold churches to watch perfect strangers get married.

"Someday that'll be you," she whispers.

I'm supposed to want to be the bride, but picture myself more as the priest, holy and dignified, neutral. I like the crisp white collar, asexual demeanor, purported closeness with God, but have learned to keep my mouth shut. Meanwhile, my mother is obsessed with marrying me off, weddings being her favorite extreme sport. There's no room in her agenda for fantasies about priests. She trains me hard: double sessions, field trips to parishes named for specific saints.

Each time a new bride stands at the ready, my mother cries into a wadded Kleenex.

"So beautiful," she says, which isn't true.

Some brides are scrawny with beaky noses. Some are heavy with wiry curls sprayed into a nest. Other brides are just plain homely. Still, my mother can detect the beauty in any girl about to be given away to a man. And we both know that it's me she sees in that long white dress with matching veil and shoes. Not a stranger, but her daughter. Me, flanked by a line-up of broad-shouldered attendants clad in taffeta and men in rented shoes.

In Italy, as in my corner of Western New York, wedding

receptions are a birthright: soggy macaroni and chicken thighs. DJ'd music and an open bar.

My mother can't wait to show me off to the crowd of whiskery *gumbas*, my great aunts, who magically appear at every reception. "*That's* who knows about marriage," my mother says when the old women stand to dance the tarantella. This is their blessing on every bride, their warning for every groom, the promise of what awaits him. Watching from a distance, I can feel the weight of their swollen, stomping feet, their arthritic, clapping hands.

Long ago, they let me in on the secret of matrimony: that a man (my father, say, or one of my brothers) can be stupid enough to believe he is king when everyone knows that women rule. Italian women, that is.

I nod and feign interest.

"You too!" Aunt Peppie points a gnarled finger. "No faking."

I believe her because I've seen her do magic. She and her sisters, Nonnie included, can make headaches go away by dripping oil into water and saying *mal'occhio*, the evil eye. (*Mumbo-jumbo*, my father calls it.) Any one of the sisters from Calabria can snap a rabbit's neck in half, skin it, and fry it with greens for a delicious dinner. Probably they're witches—Italian witches, of course, the good kind.

Their predictions come true.

Unable to shake off Aunt Peppie's words as I walk the halls of junior high, I find myself agreeing to go out with a boy who's been my friend since seventh grade. Not Italian. It might not actually matter, I decide, since for years I've resigned myself to an eerie certainty that nuptials (like train wrecks and cancer) are what await other people—my cousins, my brothers—not me. At the time, anyway, my secret emergency back-up plan is to join a convent, but somehow, I end up a lesbian anyway.

Imagine my surprise, twenty-five years later, when Massachusetts, a state in which by utter chance I'm living, makes it legal for people like me to marry.

"Are you sure?" I ask my partner. We watch the news on New

England Cable. "Do you think it's really going to happen?"

I never figured on becoming a twenty-first century bride.

SOMETHING OLD

My coming of age occurs in the early '80s, an era of acquiescence and yuppies. Mornings, my mother curls my hair with a hot iron, picks out pastel clothing, and talks *at* me until I begin to want what she wants. Forced into lacy anklets and patent-leather shoes long after other kids are wearing jeans, I lurch haltingly out the door each day, the first of many surrenders toward my overlong, illustrious career as a heterosexual.

My mother is happy at first, elaborately dressing me up for Friday night dinners with my new awkward boyfriend, his parents, and a sister who's as blonde as he is. They're Episcopalians from Maine and Illinois, practiced at eating fish dinners without ever once belching aloud or breaking out into a quarrel.

Their serious, whispery voices alone are miracles to me.

Studying my boyfriend's family, I learn to speak low and order salad with buttermilk dressing. It feels like a science experiment. In time, my mother will grow to fear them, these un-Italians, who might just succeed in taking me away, and yet I love them. They talk *to* me, never once mentioning marriage, my hair, or my odds of becoming homecoming queen. They're teachers, who know things; they discuss nuclear weapons, the economy, saving the environment, plans for our high school careers and beyond. Their sole agenda is their son's happiness.

For adults, they seem remarkably unafraid.

When it finally dawns on my mother that I've been adopted by this kindly Anglo tribe, she says, "He's not good enough." In her mind, I'm Jacqueline Kennedy with princes and presidents *en route* for my hand. But she's one-hundred percent wrong about the boy I've chosen.

Nerdy and sweet, he's endlessly patient with my hesitancy about romance. "You don't have to do anything you don't want," he tells me. "It doesn't matter." Whenever I'm near him, I listen for the blood pumping through his body, striving to open the clenched fist that is my own heart, to feel what other people feel. I spend the summer doing research, lying on the front porch reading *Anna Karenina*, wondering if love has to be that hard. Every night I get on my knees and pray to Jesus, "Please let it happen tomorrow. Amen."

At last, there's an answer. I fall in love.

From the age of thirteen until I'm about to turn twenty-two, this tall blonde boy is my one-and-only, my heartthrob, sidekick, my entire world. He and I grow up together, navigating our stormy adolescent emotions and dreams, exploring the electric thrill of our bodies together. We take a trip to California to visit his grandmother. We're comfortable socializing together with adults and friends, but we steal away alone whenever possible. We laugh. To my mother's great pride, we are actually (unbelievably) voted Homecoming King and Queen. He's the only boy I can ever imagine loving—and, as we move toward adulthood and college, the only man.

With no arrangements to include other people in our sacred twosome, I'm stung when he goes to a dance with some nameless sorority sister and starts acting distant. "Date someone," my friends back at school advise. I do. I go to dinner with a couple of nice guys.

On a lark, my senior year, I start going to movies offered by the American Culture Department with my bisexual roommate.

"You only come to the lesbian films?" says my writing professor and mentor, Paul Russell; he teaches the class, a first of its kind. "People are going to talk." I'm the straightest, squarest person we know, so it's a funny joke. But standing there, laughing with him, it hits me who I might really be.

Within weeks, I stop caring if my boyfriend dates other girls; I fall in love with a girl of my own. A woman, actually, my major advisor, who's technically not even gay, she claims.

It happens so fast, there isn't time to pray.

Here's a memory, a terrible one.

I'm standing with my childhood boyfriend in my bedroom at home. It's December 1987, the first few minutes of Christmas break, our senior year in college. We've just driven home from school with his father and grandfather, and I'm trying to tell him something important. I can no longer be his girlfriend.

"I have to see this other thing through," I'm saying.

I've been telling him about the gay movies I've been watching and my theoretical sexuality since Thanksgiving, but he insists it doesn't matter; we can get married anyway.

There is a look in his eye, alternating between fierceness and defeat. He listens hard, as if I am speaking a new language.

Then, suddenly, like a shade snapping open, he understands. He knows not only what I'm saying, but what I mean.

I'm no longer his.

It's surprising the way his knees buckle, the way he falls silently to my pink shag rug like a grown man taken down by a bullet. He's twenty-two years old, 6'4", and nearly 200 pounds. He lands just a few inches from the canopy bed where we've been together when no one is home. He doesn't utter a sound, only looks out the window as if there might be a message etched there in the dark pane.

I try to decipher it myself.

I'm so young, so optimistic. How can I know that it'll be at least a decade before he speaks to me again?

Like a caliph bowing deeply on a prayer rug, my suddenly former boyfriend rests his forehead against the carpet in surrender.

Then he stands up and leaves.

SOMETHING NEW

The next time true love makes an appearance in my life, it's late one night in 1999. I'm watching a rerun of Oprah while visiting friends in Berkeley after a harrowing year-long break-up with a woman who has broken my heart and stolen my money. My adult life has been characterized by a series of bad romantic choices. Perhaps I've just been unlucky, though I sometimes wonder if I'm choosing to punish myself.

This particular night in California, I'm sprawled across a strange futon in a spare apartment reserved for married graduate students. It's a few days before Christmas, the last Noël of the 20th Century, and I'm thirty-three years old, depressed, and jetlagged. In an overcrowded world of 5.8 billion people, I feel utterly and hopelessly alone.

Flipping the channels, I happen upon one TV talk show after another. The topic on Oprah is etiquette, but I stay tuned anyway because her theme song cheers me up. "O" is for openness. Optimism! All I really have to do, I realize, is get through the holidays: another hour, this evening, the rest of my life. How hard could it be with Oprah always there to rely upon at 3 a.m., ready with her pragmatic advice? I watch commercials for mascara, feminine pads, rejuvenating shampoo.

When the show returns, I find myself suddenly staring into my future.

I sit up, pointing. "Hey!" I tell the scraggly house plants that are my only company. "There she is!" *She* is Meryl Cohn, a writer I've met on several occasions.

I've sat across from her—Thanksgiving, Fourth of July, New Year's—at tables of fellow writers. Still, I've never actually *looked* at her before. Now, on TV, she exudes sex appeal and confidence. Even Oprah seems won over by her charm: green eyes, auburn hair, the cheekbones of a 1940s movie star.

During a brief Q& A, edited to one Q (*Should straight people ever ask gay people if they are gay?*), Meryl chats easily, explaining to the studio audience how to know when something is offensive. She offers a quick rundown of the *dos* and *don'ts* of queer etiquette. Joking about the age-old question, "What do women like in bed?" Meryl says wryly, "Other women, of course."

Oprah, lovely and velvety, responds with a deep-throated laugh.

Then, in a flash, the magic passes, and she's just someone I've met, friend of a friend, on Lifetime Television for Women: only Meryl author of the syndicated tongue-in-cheek advice column Ms. Behavior. It's just as well. I'm not looking for thunderbolts. I can barely manage a change of clothes.

Closing my eyes, I sink back into my familiar funk. My life is a troubling narrative, but at least I know what to expect: bad choices, difficult women, anxiety, despair. I fall asleep to the sound of the TV, cozy in my misery, unaware that somewhere not far away, a perfect stranger is taking my life into her hands.

Messages are being received—and some of them, it turns out, are about me.

Back in New York in February, I seek out Meryl's advice about a woman I'm casually dating. (Meryl *is* an advice columnist, after all, and it's obvious I could use some help.) It turns out she is in town for a few weeks, so we arrange to meet at a gay bookstore in lower Manhattan, now sadly defunct. I launch into my problem without prelude.

"Dump her," Meryl says.

She brings up a little story of her own, how her good friend Linda Brown has been receiving messages about her from someone in California. "My friend Psychic Mary wants me to tell you that you've already met your new girlfriend," Linda tells her. "Psychic Mary sees books."

Meryl doesn't know the woman making these predictions about her future. "I *have* a girlfriend, thank you very much." Her relationship is troubled, but she's loyal, nonetheless.

Linda Brown claims she is only passing messages. "Psychic Mary hears voices. Are you going to argue with voices?"

We laugh off the prediction over tea.

Linda Brown has said something else that Meryl won't tell me until months later: a prediction about our getting married, Linda herself the maker of the wedding cake.

It's the turn of a new century, but even so, a prediction of marriage seems absurdly far from reality. The world is hardly our oyster. Even if it were, Meryl is not exactly the blushing-bride type, which is part of her allure.

Meryl strikes me as definitely attractive, but I fancy myself too short for her. I am 5'3", a good seven inches shy of matching her height. Even so, after that bookstore meeting, I invite her to lunch, the movies, dinner. Each time I share my latest adventure: a blind date who is actually blind, a woman who wants to take me camping after one cup of coffee, a trainer who asks me out for kick-boxing and dinner. I'm trying to renew my childhood faith in love; also, I'm lonely. My stories make Meryl laugh.

Between us we have two Seven Sister degrees, two Masters' degrees, a couple of literary grants, one very successful advice column, two published books, and four books-in-progress. We're not exactly dumb. It's just we're unaccustomed to living out someone else's narrative, a psychic's no less. Who believes in voices, anyway—coming from where, the great beyond?

In my life so far, all predictions have turned out wrong. Love has been a disaster. My only good relationship happened in puberty with a boy who doesn't speak to me.

Using tickets I can't get rid of, I take Meryl to Puccini's *Butterfly*—by chance, on Valentine's Day. And despite the fact that there is nothing like Italian opera to spur on romance, we manage to keep up our ignorance.

To reciprocate, she invites me to Eve Ensler's *Vagina Monologues*.

"Are you kidding?" I say, the guise of friendship beginning to wear.

We spend the entire following Sunday together. After the *Monologues*, we walk downtown in the rain, eat Mexican, cruise a bookstore. Sitting in the self-help aisle, we diagram each other's personalities, confess our biggest flaws. At a coffee shop around the corner, I grill her about her talk show tour. Flashing back to that lonely California night on a borrowed futon, I can't bring myself to mention her TV appearance, my premonition.

Walking down the street, I'm suddenly aware of how tall Meryl is; how wide the world, how mysterious. For the first time since junior high, I'm truly afraid. But here it is: late and chilly on a dark street corner in Chelsea, my future unraveling before me. I'm afraid to believe that there are good endings in the works.

Wary, I look into Meryl's eyes, suddenly feeling the power and danger of love. I get a new glimpse at how it is that Anna Karenina ended up under that train.

SOMETHING BORROWED

I go for long stretches without hearing from Meryl. It turns out Ms. Behavior practices what she preaches: no hint of a new relationship will be permitted until her current one comes to its natural conclusion.

Not to worry, my shrink reassures me: "There is no cure for love."

House with a swing, Psychic Mary continues her predictions. *A life together, growing old.*

May 17, 2004, 8:30 a.m., a raw morning in Cape Cod, Massachusetts, Meryl and I stand waiting to fill out some paperwork. It is the first day that gays can legally be married, and we have the first appointment. A line is already forming, couples standing shoulder to shoulder on the steps of town hall.

By nine a.m., the streets are filled. Hundreds of onlookers watch and wait, cheering. People throw confetti, take photographs. Some carry signs; others hand out roses to every bride, male or female. Volunteers from the Human Rights Campaign cut wedding cake for any two waving a license to marry. The festive atmosphere harkens back to earlier days: the first Gay Pride parades in New York City, the Marches on Washington, the 1980's, the 1990's.

Though now we are decades from our youth and our friends are no longer dying in droves.

"This one's pretty," my mother says about Meryl. She likes her on first sight because Meryl is a knockout, and my mother is vain. She's come a long way since the days of hysterical crying, breast-beating, throwing herself at me, when she tried everything, from daily novenas to not looking at me to begging me to go back to the boyfriend I had in high school and college. She hasn't cornered me in the kitchen to tell me she wants to be the only woman in my life, or attacked my ugly short hair in years. We're in much easier daily contact, thanks to the computer given for her 70th birthday.

Handing over our paperwork, Meryl and I race up the Cape to Orleans District Court, where we pay for our waiver of the three-day waiting period, an arcane hold-over from the days of syphilis and shotgun weddings, when a few days of clarity might have made a difference. (Formerly $65, this waiver now costs $195, the special homosexual rate.) Greeting us in chambers is Judge Welch, a small, worn New Englander in formal robes, like the other Judge Welch's before him—his father and grandfather.

This Judge Welch keeps his office dark and smelling of cherry tobacco.

"I'm pleased to take part in this special day." His eyes twinkle. He presses our hands into his small binding grip. "This day, your day, of love."

We hold our breaths. Here we are: among the first gay people to marry in the United States of America, in the first state to go legal, on the 50th anniversary of Brown v. the Board of Education.

"An auspicious day for civil rights!" the judge says, breaking into a smile.

Returning to Provincetown for our final license, we are greeted by an army of television cameras. Over the past few weeks, we've turned down media requests from *Newsday* to TV Japan, politely declining reporters who want to follow us around to document our wedding day. We're camera-shy. Still, the local news catches our happy moment, which runs in a continuous loop on the *New York Times* website.

We head for home.

At four o'clock, we're married in our living room by someone we've only just met. After Republican Governor Mitt Romney has made sure that friends of gay people are not swiftly deputized and pressed into service, we hire a lovely, elderly, gay African-American minister who walks up our steep steps with a cane. She speaks solemnly of candles and circles and unions. It feels suddenly meaningful to participate in an institution designed for our exclusion, more so than expected. It's funny how one can be unaware of one's oppression until the instant it's lifted.

We read our vows.

Flown in from New York, Meryl's brother is our witness, ring bearer, flower boy. Her sister calls a few moments after we've taken our vows; my new father-in-law and his wife phone that evening. Meryl's mother sends flowers.

From my family, there is only silence. On May 17th, well through the following Sunday, when our marriage is announced in the *New York Times*, I hear nothing.

I can feel my mother's grief, but I fight it.

All my life, I've struggled against absorbing her quiet devastation. Surrounded by my dearest and queerest friends, I feel happy, lucky, proud. I wish I could somehow show my mother that I am not so different from who I used to be.

If there were queerleaders, I'd still be captain.

My life is a testament to this fact: At college, I helped start a lesbian and gay alumnae group; in New York, I helped some friends to die and others to live. I'm quoted about things queer in the *Wall Street Journal* and *Newsweek*. I published a collection of short stories, changed from the original title of *Nuclear Family and Other Fictions* to *Lucy on the West Coast and Other Lesbian Short Fiction* by a publisher keen to expand the market.

And yet, when I think about my family, I still feel bad. I

imagine them opening the paper to our smiling newsprint faces, cringing each time the word *lesbian* appears in the inky text.

Later, a former girlfriend and teaching colleague expresses her disapproval over our little miraculous publication. "I expected to find your name in the *Book Review Section*," she says, "not in *Styles*."

My parents also make their embarrassment known. When I probe for details, they offer terseness. "Yeah, we saw it."

Other friends seem puzzled by our public wedding announcement in the newspaper of record, and want to know how we pulled it off, as if Meryl and I have somehow managed to fool the press.

When the moment arrives, of course, none of it matters. Not even my mother.

"Do you take this woman?" the minister asks.

And I do. Completely and happily, I do.

SOMETHING BLUE

Italians may not be big fans of the lesbian, but they do love a good party. Hence my mother's dilemma. I can practically feel her blanch at the thought of her relatives crossing state lines to dance the tarantella at my queer wedding.

Since Meryl and I don't want (can't afford) a traditional reception, we decide to have two small parties: one in New York in June and one on Cape Cod in September.

My mother comes to both.

In New York, the party is at our best friends', Kenny and David's, apartment on Central Park South, overlooking the park. Meryl's friend Linda Brown makes a fantastical wedding cake from scratch, towering layers with four fillings and a cascade of purple orchids. (Somewhere in California a psychic is smiling.)

Accompanying my mother are two homophobic brothers, with their girlfriend and wife. My father neither comes to the wedding nor acknowledges it. I try to prepare my mother as much as I can, telling her that Meryl's family is happy for us, that she should be happy too.

With lingering trepidation, I prepare myself as well.

My family arrives late. My brothers stand around in the corner, drinking beer, one of them in a baseball cap and sneakers. ("Kind of hot!" Kenny says of him, trying to put a good spin on the situation.)

My brothers can't seem to stop gawking at our forty dearest friends, though they manage to refrain from making homophobic jokes. As I catch them passing shocked glances twice during the toast, I realize that they have never been in a room with so many gay people. To them, this party—my life—is a spectacle.

My mother is more at ease; she receives daily emails about my queer life. She circulates, chatting with everyone, recognizing names and details. Now, when we hang up the phone, we both say that we love each other; we both mean it.

Only when Debbie, my former college roommate, arrives with her husband, do my brothers and my mother truly come to life. They pump her husband's hand, questioning her about her kids, the suburbs. For a happy moment, they locate me in Debbie, the me they know from when I belonged to my ex-boyfriend; she was a girl with a future they understood.

Later, in a corner, while talking to Meryl's father, my mother cries. She tells him how disappointed she is at my father's lack of interest, at the fact that her only daughter, her baby, is gay. Several friends overhear her admit that her own nintey-two-year-old mother is more accepting of my lesbianism than she is. I know it's true; from the haze of her nursing home decline, Nonnie has repeatedly told my mother she should be happy that I have found someone to love.

Even so, at the end of the evening, my mother looks around at my friends and says, "I didn't know you had so many *people*." For Italians this is a high compliment, meaning people who love you. It's almost as good as praising the food at a wedding. Which she also does.

Despite her public tears, I am proud of my mother for her struggle. I take it as a sign that our relationship is alive and well.

Our second wedding party is just as magical as our first despite a September hurricane on the Cape: Ivan the Terrible. Our host is our dear friend Lynda who opens her beautiful home on the Pamet River to our friends and family. My mother attends with my sister-in-law and my sister-in-law's best friend. (My brothers have apparently had enough of my gay friends to last a lifetime.) During the speeches and readings, my mother sits across the room like an outsider; she seems smaller than before, vulnerable. Several of my chivalrous lesbian friends from Brooklyn attend to her every need, refilling her drink, chatting with her about the weather.

The next morning at brunch, my mother and my sister-in-law stay only a few minutes, eager to get started on their ten-hour drive.

My mother gives Meryl and me a gift, her mother's China.

"Nonnie always wanted you to have it," she says, looking away.

As I walk my mother down to the car, a terrible thing happens. The hem of her denim skirt gets caught on the heel of her rubber sandal and she takes a nasty spill down a long, narrow set of wooden stairs off the deck.

My mouth goes dry.

Standing on the top step, looking down at her sprawled across the landing, my heart lurches. This is my seventy-two-year-old mother, a woman I've loved and disappointed all my life. Irrationally, I feel I'm to blame for this fall.

Back on her feet in a flash, she brushes herself off, blaming her outfit. I rush down the steps, choking back tears, and hug her for as long as she'll let me.

"I'm sorry," I tell her.

Sorry about everything.

And I am.

And I'm not.

WHAT GETS PASSED ON

THE LAST TIME I see my father, it's snowing.

The weather brings me back to childhood—blizzards often do—a dark sky opening overhead, the sting of icy air, and a feeling that the world has drawn together under one ominous fate— predicted and announced on the evening news.

In the snow, I'm a kid, small and curious, looking up at clouds and endless dizzying flakes. I like belonging to something—even if it is just snow.

But I'm not young anymore; I'm forty-two, happily married, and living in another state.

It's early in January, 2009, a few hours before dawn.

I've been visiting my parents in Western New York to help my seventy-six-year-old mother after an operation that removes her remaining ovary, which she's fond of calling her second hysterectomy. The surgery seems unnecessary to me, a non-cancerous cyst that has grown only slightly, but no one asks, so I don't say.

Everything goes surprisingly well. By the second day, she's up and around. My two brothers who live locally stop by in the evening to eat whatever my father and I have cooked up during the day.

Things seem easier with him than they've ever been.

The past few years, the family dinner table has been a minefield. My father and brothers are conservative; my mother and I are progressive. Goading is their sport; dodging is ours. It's a game we've played much of our adult lives in ever inching extremes, but no one seems in the mood. Even my volatile father is mellow, having switched from his usual gin to wine.

Over the years, I've learned to navigate my parents' home.

Ours has always been the only stately colonial on the block with guns in display cases. Even after we're grown and gone, the guns pop up in unlikely places: behind hanging clothes in closets or stacked in piles under the bed in the guest room. Animal heads mounted on walls and lamp stands made of deer hooves still make a person worry about stepping out of line. A life-size carousel horse sits in the middle of our family room near an authentic barber's chair with a red leather seat, and a large wooden dog wearing a bow tie who affably extends a tray to hold your drink.

My mother's untouched decor from the 70s—glass and chrome, velvet wallpaper, orange shag rugs—does little to help. It's a bit like stepping back in time. The whole mishmash adds up to the confusion I've come to think of as childhood.

The last night of my visit, we cling to a safe topic—the weather.

A worrisome blizzard is heading our way. With one Great Lake north and another west, my hometown is always ready for an emergency. You don't mess around in these parts; you change your travel plans.

My Dad and I are up early hoping I can beat the storm.

We pack my car to prepare for the slippery five-and-a-half-hour drive back to Massachusetts. I have my reliable travel companion, Violette Leduc, a gentle but athletic black standard poodle the family fawns over. Dad insists I take lunch in his hunting cooler, which he's put together for me himself. He's never been much of gift giver, at least not to me, save for a bike on my 12th birthday, and, once, when I was on a break home from college, he taught me to shoot a rifle at the Farm.

"You can have it if you want," he said, handing the gun over.

I nailed the target, bruised my shoulder, and probably insulted him when I declined. "I don't think they allow guns on campus."

There is also my college education, paid for in full.

My chest fills with cold air and gratitude.

Here's the man who's given me life, and however difficult our past has been, he isn't going to be around forever. I scrape ice off the windshield, stomp snow off my boots.

"I love you, Dad."

The silence that follows is awkward.

I whistle for Violette, who's out in the pitch-black yard, nosing for squirrels. Together, we watch her bound toward us over snowbanks, agile and graceful as she slides through the beams of the car's headlights and leaps into the back seat.

In the dark, my father clears his throat. "I love you, too."

Three months later he's dead.

It happens while he's chopping down a tree 40 miles north of my family's home. The coroner calls his death instantaneous: an exploding aorta. A female jogger finds him while trespassing on the trailed hunting land my father still owns, the place he loves most on earth.

He would be furious at the jogger's intrusion if only his body weren't slumped over the three-wheel ATV he uses for motoring around his wooded kingdom. Though I don't know it at the time, this land—the farm my dad bought in 1970—is about to become the focus of my disinheritance.

No one in my family sees it coming.

When it's time to deal with the will, they panic and pretend it's missing. This effort, they later say, is to protect me. But it turns out you can't keep a daughter from reading her father's will. I call the lawyer who wrote the will—my childhood friend Steven's dad, it turns out—who apologizes in an email with a copy attached.

In the will, my father has put my mother's name on the deed to the house and has made her the beneficiary of his dwindling investments, leaving the rest of his estate to my three older brothers. It's an act accomplished in a single sentence: "I leave no bequest to my daughter for reasons known to her." He's even happened on legal phrasing similar to what Joan Crawford used to disinherit her daughter Christina, author of the later tell-all autobiography, "Mommie Dearest."

My first response is to laugh: my macho Italian-American father emulating a Hollywood diva. But I'm in shock, a temporary state. I brace myself for the pain and humiliation I've spent a lifetime trying to outrun.

I can feel it out there—unavoidable, crippling, headed in my direction.

My second response is to cry. For weeks. Being disinherited feels like a baseball bat to the back of the neck—jarring, violent, disorienting.

For relief, I turn to my spouse, my friends, my therapist. I join a twelve-step spiritual program for people affected by family alcoholism and start a serious yoga practice to see if I can twist away the pain.

When all else fails, I turn to Google.

I find out that disinherited people are everywhere—in the news, in historical documents, literature, other people's families—a whole silent population of the suffering and disavowed. There's Cordelia and Jane Eyre, of course, but also real-life characters. How have I landed in such a natural sisterhood with Jane Fonda, Jamie Lee Curtis, Tori Spelling, Paris Hilton? I'm not even blond. I learn that only in America do parents routinely disinherit their children without any legal or judicial checks and balances. In most of the rest of the world, the act itself—personally, morally, legally, and culturally—is practically unimaginable. In other places, where it exists at all, it's highly regulated by a dissuasive judicial process.

"But isn't it mostly assholes who expect an inheritance anyway?" A friend says over lunch one day. "And who get one?"

The look on her face is one I've seen before when the topic of my disinheritance comes up. "You think?"

"It's a privilege thing, you wouldn't understand; you grew up middle-class. I grew up working-poor. People like me have parents who have debt to pass down."

I think about this. "It's not like I was sitting around expecting an inheritance."

"No?" she says.

"No!" I wonder if this is true. "I mean, I wasn't expecting I'd be *dis*inherited. It's like getting cut out of the family, not just a will."

She shrugs. "Don't ask me. I expect nothing from anyone."

"Maybe not, but I bet you'll leave your kids an inheritance," I say pointedly. "My Dad is like you; he came from immigrants who worked in factories. He only got to the middle class because someone else paid for his medical school."

The conversation has touched a nerve, so we change the subject to writing.

I want to tell her that soon Baby Boomers (and their parents) will fork over approximately $46.5 trillion to the next generations. That this unprecedented transfer of wealth means that more than half of all Americans will receive an inheritance—a percentage derived *after* adjusting for class and race. That's a lot of people; they can't all be assholes, can they?

I don't want to sound like one myself, so I shut up.

Money is never an easy topic since white people control it, mostly men. That said, disinheritance is not unfamiliar among LGBTQI folks, who have been getting kicked out of families and cut out of wills for centuries.[1]

Other people look beyond the money and marvel, instead, at the emotional impact. They say it's unthinkable that my father walked into a lawyer's office with premeditated malice and carried out his intent to erase me from his legacy. This response also surprises me,

---

[1] Paul Revere, for example, disinherited one of his many grandsons, a pottery shop owner who'd changed his name from butch Frank to soft Francis—a name reserved for women in the Revere family. What "fun" homophobic and/or transphobic historians have had with this information, writing about Francis Revere as a probable "Sissy," or "Nancy boy."

because I tend to steel myself for the question I sometimes get and always imagine others are thinking: *What did you do to your father that made him disinherit you?*

For me, it's hard to hold onto how outrageous and psychologically violent the act of disinheriting a child is. And yet U.S. laws still support it.

Why did it happen to me? I suspect in part I've always been the wrong kind of offspring, a girl. I don't share many of my family's beliefs or hobbies and am never the type to hold back an opinion.

Also, I've found the love of my life, a woman, and married her, though my family refutes that this is the reason.

"He didn't care about you enough for that to matter," one brother says.

Another suspects it's because I'm the youngest and the last to work out my issues with Dad. "Shit rolls downhill," the second brother tells me.

For verification, I write to my father's lawyer, who says Dad never explicitly said why he was doing it. "I assume because you're gay," he writes in an email—he, who once tried to drown his own gay son in the toilet. "But sadly, I never asked."

Had I lived in the same hometown as my parents, married a man, and had a bunch of children, would my father have disinherited me? Research on disinheritance (although meager, faulty, and outdated) seems to indicate that moving away from home—whether a person is gay or straight—is the one thing most disinherited adult children have in common.

"Then why *did* Dad disinherit me?" I ask my mother, who says she also doesn't think it's because I'm a lesbian.

She points to a stormy back-and-forth of letters, dating to nearly twenty years earlier, a frank exchange about childhood sexual abuse that was without precedent.

"But we made up after that!" I say. "We moved beyond it, didn't we? I feel like we did. I did, anyway." The older you get, the more you understand that we are, most of us, just struggling to be better versions of ourselves. You forgive, focus on what's really important—love, maybe.

Meryl and her friend Donna take me to an Al-Anon meeting. I return all that spring and summer. During the autumn of my disinheritance, on a Saturday in October 2009, I am somehow asked to speak at an annual twelve-step convention in Provincetown for people in recovery, called the "Round Up," though I have never spoken in any of the three groups I attend each week. For the main event on Saturday evening, about 1,500 LGBTQ people gather under a huge tent to listen to two speakers from AA and one from Al-Anon (me), who share experience, strength, and hope.

When it's my turn, I describe my father and my childhood, the confusion surrounding my disinheritance.

I list the things I do to recover from emotional despair: grieve, mostly; learn to pray for real, pass as much time in meetings and on yoga mats as possible, commit to a spiritual program. I talk about how Frida Kahlo is my stand-in Higher Power until I can work my way up to a "God of my understanding," as the program puts it, which eventually does happen, a true spiritual awakening, as promised in the literature. I find a bit of compassion for my father, my brothers, my mother, myself; it's something like forgiveness. As close as I can get.

What I've learned most, I tell the crowd, is to adjust my expectations and attitudes. The best way I can think to sum this up is by repeating a Leonard Cohen lyric: *Love is not a victory march, it's a cold and it's a broken Hallelujah.* When I finish speaking, some of the audience members jump to their feet; everyone joins in—a standing ovation.

Surprised by this reception, I suddenly see that I belong exactly where I'm standing—in my own shoes.

"We love you," someone shouts from the crowd of strangers who embrace me because of my struggle, because of my hope.

Then, a thought, a realization that has taken a lifetime; I step back up to the microphone and say it aloud to my community.

"You are my inheritance."

I still think an awful lot about that final morning with my father; I picture myself standing there trying to see his face in the dark. I replay our goodbye hug in that place of my birth, the city where my mother and father were born, got married, raised children, and ran my father's practice; where my brothers listened to bootlegs of *The Grateful Dead* and roamed around as freely as princes—a place I have tried to leave behind time and again, but never can, not entirely.

The last time I saw him, I was driving away, a familiar landscape of snow whizzing past my window, filling my rearview mirror.

I was already making plans to return, to pick up where we'd left off, to see how far "I love you" would take us.

I felt hope rising: it was going to be different next time, better.

LONG RUN

"I want to write rage but all that comes is sadness…"
—Audre Lorde

TEACH THIS TO YOUR HEART

I DON'T KNOW ABOUT birds, or what they mean.

I know about dogs, by which I mean my dog, singular. She arrives with black cottony fur in the dead of winter and grows up fast and tall and funny, the way standard poodles do.

The little cough seems like nothing at first. "Allergies," the vet says. Small and breathy, it gets louder. The vet changes her mind. "GERD?"

I want to tell her about working for the advertising guy who invented GERD, but the X-ray shows a curved white spine like a toy railroad track, easy to break, and a set of cage bars with something caught inside, her heart.

The ghostly outline from the light box looks like a loaf of bread.

"That's the tumor in her lung," the vet says. She traces it with her finger. "Very rare in dogs. They don't smoke."

Violette Leduc, standard poodle, stands watching wide-eyed. Not because this is bad news, her diagnosis of lung cancer, but because it is how she approaches the world. She has always been open to everything, until the very end when food stops going down. We give her cat food by hand: smelly little bites.

We sit with Violette on the porch all spring, and people from the block come by to see her. She has friends we hardly know, a social life of her own. She's gotten invited to dinners and barbeques—I'm not kidding—and once a ride in a canoe across a pond we later learn about from a picture: She's manning the bow, nose forward. There are even cat people who, on meeting her, think they might actually not mind a dog. We know but don't say that the only one they really want is her. Particular soul, she is a canine Gandhi who believes in peace—she's never had a scuffle, fight, or argument.

By June, she is still running in the park, each sprint shorter than the last.

It gets hot in July, even under the cherry tree we've planted in the front yard, which has finally grown up to stretch its branches enough to give off shade. She practices her downward position and rests there, keeping an eye out for neighbor kids, for rabbits and squirrels.

After surviving her final fireworks on the 4th—no bother at all, for once—she stops running altogether. Too soon it is a memory: taking laps, sprinting toward, and galloping away, ears back, tongue unfurled against white teeth, smiling. She's loved running on beaches and trails, in parks. Seeing her in motion, I've often thought I understood how God must feel when some poor fool like me suddenly figures out why she's been sent here: to love or to write or to pray.

The kids down the street say their final goodbyes. Patting her head, they look her in the eye to see what dying is all about—an eventuality so far away, it must seem made up by adults.

That Friday morning it rains, but when the vet shows up in an eggplant-colored van with a younger woman in tow, her assistant, the sun comes out. She gently suggests we say goodbye outside. I don't want to—it's wet—but can't come up with a convincing excuse, so we all spread out blankets and carry Violette to the shade under the cherry tree, bed, and all.

She barely weighs a thing. You can see every rib, her collarbones, and the place where her hip connects to her leg, a sunken socket. I have worried so much about this moment, but she is too tired for an emotional goodbye: All she does when the time comes is lay her head down and close her eyes. The night before, she let us know it was time by making sure her four paws were touching us both at the same time.

When she is gone, the vet covers her with a blanket, carries her to the van, and takes her away.

Meryl and I sit on the porch together, but alone now. After a few minutes, a cardinal lands on a nearby branch, burbling out a song for us. We marvel at his whistles and trills. It seems he'll never stop.

Amazed, we don't speak, just clasp hands.

On Monday, at the end of a yoga class, a teacher reads a poem while we rest in dead man's pose. By chance, it is Mary Oliver's "Red Bird Explains Himself." Perfect for me to hear since I still need to understand.

This was my true task, to be the/music of the body. Do you understand? the red bird in the poem explains his presence. *For truly the body needs/a song, a spirit, a soul. And no less, to make this work,/ the soul has need of a body,/and I am both of the earth, and I am of the inexplicable/beauty of heaven/where I fly so easily, so welcome, yes.*

It stops my breath.

And this is why I have been sent, says the red bird, *to teach this to your heart.*

Many mornings that summer and fall, I stand under Violette's cherry tree, trying to recall the exact details of her gentle passing. *We should all be so blessed,* I think when I realize a black-capped chickadee has hatched her babies in the little birch birdhouse we've hung on a nearby fence post.

I can hear them screaming their tiny baby-bird heads off, as if to announce their arrival, their unbearable hunger for life.

THE LONELINESS OF THE COVID
LONG HAULER

I AM RUNNING UNDER a canopy of trees on a path near my home in Western Mass.

On my left is a wooded hill owned by Smith College; on my right, the rangy Mill River. This week, *The New York Times* has published an article asserting that runners are safe not wearing masks. The odds of transmitting SARS-CoV-2 are low due to the circulation of so much fresh air.

I wear a mask anyway.

I have been extra cautious about COVID, because of Meryl's immune system, her lungs. We isolate ourselves: no stores, no gyms, no grocery markets. We wipe down each purchase before bringing it inside. We bleach doorknobs, gate latches, and the mailbox.

We scrub our hands raw.

Running is sacrosanct, a thing I do that Meryl doesn't. There's nothing else as good for my brain, mood, and muscles. It's even better now that traffic has disappeared. My lungs no longer hurt when I exercise. I move like I'm 30 again, up to five, six, sometimes seven miles a day.

It's May 2020: pandemic lockdown.

Months will pass before I remember the skinny shirtless high school track team, bunched together, shiny with sweat, none of them wearing a mask. How they stream around me, passing, laughing, both elegant and awkward; I hear them pant and see acne sprinkled across their shoulders. My doctor, also a runner, will later tell me: "Prolonged exposure to an exercising group of young men who jostle past and put you in their slipstream is not what experts meant when they declared running safe."

Before shelter-in-place, Meryl and I go to Los Angeles for most of February to help her mother, whose lungs and heart are a liability. The day before we fly back home, Meryl and her brother manage the impossible, getting their mother out of the hospital and back home to her apartment, now stocked with assistive devices, food, extra oxygen tanks, and a hospital bed. They hire Josie, a full-time, live-in aide. Even so, Toby's health is rushing in a bad direction, which she acknowledges only once, obliquely, when she says she hopes that she's been both loving and loved.

"You have been," Meryl and I tell her. "You are!"

By Friday, May 15th, Toby's doctor has run out of ideas, unless Toby's willing to go to the hospital for more invasive tests and treatment. She isn't. COVID is rampant by now, and the hospital is a lonely prospect.

In a blink, the decision is made: hospice care.

That evening, Meryl and I meet the rest of our fate in a banana.

"This fruit tastes bland," I complain. "It's a *blandana*!"

Meryl laughs, my favorite sound. "You've been complaining about food for days."

I hold out my banana, and Meryl takes a bite. "Delicious!"

We laugh again. A moment passes. "Oh, shit!" we say in unison.

I run to the kitchen, open spice jars—oregano, pepper, rosemary, cardamom—but nothing breaks through.

"No taste, no smell," I say.

Meryl's face loses color.

We've made a contingency plan: quarantining can happen in the guest bedroom; she will use the half-bath downstairs except at night and for showers; I will use the upstairs bathroom, giving it a good bleaching after every use. We have emergency bottles of spray bleach within easy reach. I grab two along with some masks, a box of latex-free gloves, and a roll of paper towels and head upstairs.

"Maybe it's nothing," I say.

But in our hearts, we both know it's Coronavirus.

The guest bedroom at the top of the stairs is a nine-foot by nine-foot square with barely enough space for the double bed, dresser, and nightstand. Everything touches the soothing blue walls (a color Meryl concocted herself). To get under the covers, you have to crawl up from the foot of the bed.

Meryl leaves meals in the hallway on paper plates, along with garbage bags, plastic cutlery, and a white plastic oximeter she's purchased online.

"Clip it to your finger," she says.

The thing beeps when my blood oxygen saturation goes low: ninety-three, ninety-two, ninety-one. It goes off all the time, stopping only after I take several deep breaths, which bring my O2 level back up to at least ninety-four.

Besides the absence of taste and smell and the low oximeter reading, it feels like nothing is wrong. Thanks to all the smog-free running, my lungs are in great shape. I'm also fairly yogic for a postmenopausal person: I can balance on my hands, head, and forearms, inverting myself against walls and doors to align my spine.

Whenever Meryl hears the oximeter beeping, she calls me on my mobile phone.

"But I don't feel unoxygenated," I say.

"Breathe deeper."

We make a deal that if my O2 levels dip into the eighties, I will go to the hospital. I do deep-breathing exercises to avoid this possibility.

When Meryl's not calling or texting me, she's on the phone

with hospice administrators, doctors, and her mother or brother. Hypervigilant, I listen to her side of the conversation from behind the closed door. I listen for the sound of her cough and scan my own body constantly.

I detect a tiny headache behind my left eye, but when it lets up, I decide it was imaginary. A twinge in my lower left flank flares up, old cheerleading injury, not that unusual.

The following day, though I am not chilled or feverish, my body begins to shake uncontrollably. My eyeballs feel like sandpaper, though they spill big wet drops whenever I roll over or stand up. In the mirror, they look alarmingly red, with weird yellow ridges in a line from the pupils to the outside corners. *Manageable*, I decide. By afternoon, my neck and shoulders have seized up. The backs of my lungs constrict. My legs ache, though I barely move a muscle.

This is the beginning.

COVID, it turns out, is insidious. It doesn't care about strengths but finds vulnerabilities. Symptoms morph from one to the next, seeming to move from weak point to weak point. The cascade flows: eyes sting; head throbs; shoulders clinch; lower back aches; muscles feel weak, and hurt; arms and legs go numb, then hands and feet; stomach is sour; food seems impossible; skin bristles with heat; body blooms with rashes, toes turn red; brain fogs; cough comes and goes; throat is raw; glands swell; breath is short.

Through it all, I am oddly euphoric.

At the start of the second week, I feel so happy and jacked up that I'm almost manic, followed by a string of days without any sleep at all.

For seventy-two hours, I keep myself busy around the clock. I read a huge stack of *New Yorkers*, watch Tik-Tok videos, search for my exes' names in criminal records, find some, search the scant medical literature on COVID research, find little. When I'm finally able to sleep, my symptoms take a sharp turn toward a shooting white pain in the heart.

Angina is not a metaphor.

The oximeter starts beeping, which is confusing, because my blood-oxygen is above ninety-four. A second number is flashing, though: BPM, which means beats per minute. At 40, my number is much too low. The electronic alarm seems to get louder, and I wonder if I'm dying. In my head, I do the calculations: the hospital is about a three-minute drive, an eight-minute walk. *Can I get there?* Another stab in my chest, and I'm on my iPhone, certain I'll wake Meryl up.

"I had a bad feeling," she says, completely awake. "I knew something was wrong."

"I'm okay," I say, out of breath. "My heart feels weird, hurts."

"Get dressed," she says. "Put on two masks and meet me in the car."

"Unsafe," I say.

"Honey, you need to go the emergency room."

"Can't I ride my bike?" I ask. "I don't want to be in the car with you; what if you get it?"

"You're a little confused," she says, then repeats her instructions.

The sharp flip-flopping in my chest makes it hard to dress quickly, but in a few minutes, I'm sitting in the back seat, double masked, with the windows open, letting Meryl drive me up the street to the hospital. The air feels sharp and stinging.

The local ER is a ghost town.

It seems like I'm the only person there, save for a few nurses behind the glass reception window. I crouch down six feet from the sign that says *Check-in Here*, clutching my chest.

A guy rushes in through the electric doors and stands six feet to my side. He talks to a different woman at a different check-in window. Bent over, with his hands on knees, he seems like he's just run a marathon or made a winning touchdown in his pajamas.

We look at each other without nodding. We are the only two patients here. *Are we competitors for care? Anomalies in an empty ER? Will they help us? Has anyone else with COVID passed this way?*

I want to ask questions, but I'm hustled into a back room and hooked up to monitors. I lie moaning, watching as my heart rate slowly goes up. Oxygen steady. An X-ray of my lungs looks clear, a nurse tells me. "Runner," I whisper. She smiles.

A doctor enters: "Are you a nervous person?"

"Not a panic attack," I say, concentrating on breathing deeply enough to keep my oxygen level up so I can go home. The pain in my chest has begun to ease up. "No smell, no taste."

"Welp, I don't know what this is," he says. "But it's not COVID."

After a couple more hours, they release me and charge my insurance company for an emergency allergy attack. (Later, *Blue Cross Blue Shield of Massachusetts* zeroes out the charges based on a clinical diagnosis of COVID. A representative tells me it happens all the time in low-incidence areas. "The doctors don't recognize it," she says. "I'll fix this; you just get better, hon." Small miracle.)

It's still early in the North American pandemic.

If you're not dying, you're okay. If your lungs are clear, you don't have COVID. My friend Karin, who lives in New York City, says otherwise. She and her partner suffered from COVID in March, and Karin has already participated in clinical research, donated plasma, and volunteered to help on COVID wards. Her text says:

> If you were in New York City with those symptoms, you'd be placed in a clinical trial immediately and tapped for plasma. They may not recognize neurological COVID there, but they sure do here.

As far as I can tell, I'm the only cautionary tale in our small city. Neighbors know of our legendary vigilance. ("If you can get it," they say, "anyone can get it.") I'm also known in Ptown for getting COVID with one other person, a popular musician who gets admitted to Cape Cod Hospital, where she is intubated, extubated, and then sent home.

•

Though sequestered, I don't feel alone. Not really.

All day Meryl and I talk on the phone; at night we FaceTime. Local friends leave home-cooked meals at our back door. Clients and colleagues check in with me via email. Karin guides me through the ordeal, texting often and sending me forms to track my expanding list of symptoms. My office mate from the Northampton Writer's Mill sends me messages of hope; he says I'll get better like he did. Distant friends send cards, plants, fruit, and candles.

The real surprise is my family.

My mother calls me every morning and every evening. My oldest brother sends emails to see how I am. By now, he's sold the Farm and legally given me the fourth portion of my father's inheritance, which I take as an attempt to make things right between us. I answer his emails. My middle brother is silent, still angry about the disinheritance article in the *New York Times*, the disinheritance blog that "disparages" our family's reputation.

My youngest brother texts: "So, you got the China virus, did you?"

Home from the ER, I sleep fitfully and wake at dusk with the oddest sensation. All the nerves in my body are firing electricity, and I can sense that there's a slight separation between my charged skin and my aching muscles. *Am I awake or asleep?* Behind my eyelids is an ever-changing lightshow of yellow patterns and explosions. My flesh dissolves into layers of yellow fog floating above my body, and I have the distinct and disturbing realization that I'm not exactly real anymore.

Everything in the room is also unreal.

A bad LSD trip? Though I've never had one, good or bad.

I'm vibrating off the bed.

I force my eyes open and make myself sit up: I am awake, I am in the guest bedroom, I am tingling all over in a very unpleasant way, I am both chilled and overheated—but, basically, I'm okay.

There's something else, too, harder to explain: I grow terrified of a white tattered bathrobe hanging on the back of the door. I'm genuinely unsure whether it is a sign of some sort or whether it means to harm me. I get out of bed, shakily, pluck it off the hook, throw it on the floor. *No good.* I pick it up, put it in the closet. *Better.* The thought haunts me until I jam a chair under the closet doorknob, sure that I have saved myself from certain danger. This is the first and worst (though not last) time I experience such an alarming disruption of consciousness. After the ordeal with the bathrobe is over, my face goes numb for several hours.

Finally, on the fourteenth morning, I wake in a sweat on soaked sheets, feeling like something has ended.

This is also the day that Meryl's mom, Toby, announces she'd like a bath; then lifting her arms for an immortal embrace, she dies.

I put on clothes for the first time since the ER and walk downstairs to the front yard. The sun is bright and hurts my eyes. Meryl sits on the porch and cries. I am far away in an Adirondack chair on the lawn, trying to comfort her, but the double N95 masks stifle my voice. I realize she can't hear me at all.

A few neighbors stop over to offer condolences. Someone has texted friends, who have texted other friends. Before long there is a crowd of them standing outside our fence, along the driveway and sidewalk, a makeshift Shiva call.

Off to the side, sitting alone, I am not feeling great.

I watch a flock of geese rise in a burst across the horizon. Maybe it's a sign that Toby's soul has been set free, I think, as I fall asleep in the chair.

I'm supposed to stay in quarantine for several days following my final COVID symptoms. Since my arms, hands, legs and feet are completely numb, my throat raw, and my head throbbing, I go back upstairs and shut the door, exhausted.

For the Zoom funeral, I put on lipstick and go to my attic office.

The attic is open to the rest of the house, so I wear a mask. I stand and watch a miniature on-screen scene unfolding under a tent in an L.A. Jewish cemetery, a sad movie. Meryl's brother, Doug, his two boys, and a handful of friends gather with a rabbi to say goodbye to Meryl's larger-than-life beautiful mother, whom I understand is inside that plain pine box next to the tent. It all feels so surreal.

Toby's final words were, "I'm already dead."

"No, you're not," Doug told her. "You're still alive."

"Just wait," she said. "You'll see."

I puzzle over the meaning of this: 1) *Just wait, you'll see that I'm dead?* Or 2) *Just wait until you're dying; then you'll see what it's like?* Having had so many friends with AIDS during our years in ACT UP, I've witnessed how dying can go. Far from a linear process, it is unbearably unhurried and then suddenly over, like a slap in the face. I've read hospice workers and nurses who've seen how the dying seem to cross over and back between life and death many times before actually passing away. Often, they reach up to embrace the many souls who, they explain, have arrived to help them.

We try to keep our chins up: Toby never had to go to the hospital to die alone. I never got gravely ill. Meryl never caught COVID. Though we couldn't be in L.A. at the time of her mother's death, Meryl has been a great daughter, advocate, and companion.

As it turns out, there are actually a few things to appreciate in the shit-show of the year 2020.

I stay in quarantine for several more weeks before it's crystal clear that I'm not actually going to stop having symptoms. "You can't possibly be contagious anymore," Meryl says. "Come out now."

I wait another week.

Sometimes, I lie on the floor and listen for Baby Cass, our newest standard poodle, the littlest of our pets so far.

In the hallway she slumps against my door and sighs heavily. She needs a leader much more than any of our other dogs, and I'm it. I stick my fingers under the crack, and she pokes them gently with her nose, a little game to pass the time.

"I'll be out soon," I whisper. I train my breath to sync with hers.

Then we take a little cat nap, each on our own side of the door.

I try to suss out whether Meryl's cough is mild COVID, which would give her antibodies to keep her safe should I still be contagious when I emerge.

"I have asthma," she says. "I cough all the time. Come out of there."

Eventually I emerge from the guest bedroom and take up residency on the couch. When at last I'm able to walk a little, we sit on the porch six feet from friends. After another several months, I venture out on my own. When I see people jogging without masks, I'm enraged, fearful, sad. When maskless runners pass me and Baby Cass on our very short walks, we can't help but cross the street and hold our breath.

Eventually, everything snaps back into a more familiar version of normal.

Almost everything.

After about a year, I can finally sit up for most of the day, fueled by intermittent and often lengthy afternoon naps. In waves that grow further and further apart, I get progressively less intense versions of my original symptom cycle. When I finally have two well weeks in a row, I lie on a bolster and try to do a supported yoga pose but end up back in bed with muscle pain that makes it impossible to walk.

Even the slightest stretch gives me what they call "post-exertional malaise": a sore throat, dry cough, and lung pain with forceful gusts of exhaustion. I get these unexplained flare-ups more often than I'd like to admit, backslides that leave me desperate.

No matter that I know they are coming, any symptom-free days are cause for rejoicing and feeling stupidly optimistic. I walk around whistling and humming, positive that I'm finally all the way recovered.

That I've beaten long COVID.

•

My blog, *Literary Rejections on Display*, has been a catalogue of tongue-in-cheek content since 2007. At the very beginning of the pandemic lockdown, I decide to post videos to document a writer in captivity because it seems like a fun way to pass the time.

My first videos feature me running with masks and standing on my head, vowing to get fit during lockdown, and to finish working on a graphic novel I started. I teach myself how to use a free version of Photoshop and try to transform drawings on paper into an actual book. I joke how good it is that I'm not a gym teacher and keep up my writing from bed.

I continue to make videos, even while I'm very sick, imagining an audience of witnesses following my long COVID trajectory. Maybe the videos will help someone.

On the exact six-month mark of falling ill, I admit to the camera that I have long COVID.

It's the only video in which I cry.

No one yet knows the distance a COVID long-hauler can go.

For me, twenty-three months.

My body changes, goes soft. I hire a sweet neighbor's kid to walk the poodle. I think about taking a full-time job and giving up the hustle of the freelance life. I consider joining a clinical trial whose intervention is wearing scuba-like pants that circulate heated water around the lower half of the body for forty minutes a day, five days a week, over a period of two months, with the hope of healing the damaged epithelia.

I overhear Meryl on the phone, answering questions about how I'm doing. The irony is not lost on me that she has struggled with a rare illness for a very long time. I wonder what those calls feel like to her. Long COVID is popular; people want to know about it.

But I can't stop thinking about all the other people in the world with post-viral illness, chronic fatigue syndrome, myalgic encephalomyelitis, and other rare disease. I feel guilty having a trendy disease when they have been rendered invisible. After all, isn't my post-exertional neuroimmune exhaustion with diffuse myalgia the same as theirs?

It isn't the only thing that's unfair.

Hundreds of thousands of people have long COVID much worse than I do. Some don't have a loving partner or a family who cares enough to check in. Some are in financial trouble from medical expenses and pandemic job loss. I'm beyond fortunate and beyond grateful that I am not in any such situation.

For the most part, I manage my illness by learning to accept the limits of what I can and cannot do.

I wish I had something wise to impart. Like: I believe my suffering takes away someone else's; or I see it as my cross to bear with grace. I wish long COVID made me feel more connected to others who suffer, which, in one way or another, I guess, is all of us. But so far, I've come up empty.

There seems to be no finish line in sight.

Lying in bed, I sometimes look up from my laptop, through the window, to the soft, distant horizon, and think about the millions of souls who did not survive the virus, who died alone, terrified, in disbelief. I wonder if heartache should count as a lingering symptom of COVID.

Or maybe I have finally found the perfect vantage point from which to see that the God for whom I've searched my whole life has been here all along, a God that is simply love itself, and mercy.

AUTHOR'S NOTE

"How can you know God if you don't even know your big toe?"
—BKS Iyengar

This is a book of creative nonfiction meant to reflect the author's present recollections of experiences over time and written to emphasize certain important truths within those experiences according to her understanding of them. Most names and some characteristics have been changed, certain events have been compressed, and dialogues have been recreated. The author has chosen to use the real names of activists in the pieces titled "God is a Lesbian" and "Pharmaceutical Whore" to recognize the women who often go unacknowledged in the fight against AIDS.

The essays in this book have been published and recognized as follows:

"Cheerleader" appeared in *A Woman Like That: Lesbian and Bisexual Writers Tell Their Coming Out Stories*, edited by Joan Larkin, (New York; Avon, 1999).

"Blind Edge" appeared in *Women on the Verge*, edited by Susan Fox Rogers, (New York: St. Martin's, 1999) and was originally titled "The Rest of the Party."

A portion of "God is a Lesbian" appeared in *The Chronicle of Higher Education*, in December 2008.

"Four Days in Silence (Or, Get Me to a Nunnery)" was a finalist for a New Millennium Writings Award, and the basis for a writing grant from the Sherwood Anderson Foundation in 2004.

"This Comes Next" appeared in *Life in Provincetown Magazine (LIP)*, 2002.

"Italian Bride" was a runner-up for the Laura Coen Pizer Award and appeared in *Italian American Writers* (New York: Creative Nonfiction, 2004).

"What Gets Passed On" appeared in the *New York Times* Modern Love Column, December 11, 2011, in an altered form.

The poems "Wild Geese" and "The Journey" by Mary Oliver were reprinted here thanks to DREAM WORK, copyright ©1986 by Mary Oliver. They are being used with permission of Grove/Atlantic, Inc. Any third-party use of this material, outside of this publication, is prohibited.

Thank you to my spouse Meryl, playwright and essayist, who is forever supportive and honest about my writing, even when I want her to lie. I am so grateful for those who offered both edits and love to this work: Meryl Cohn, Mark Collins, Risa Denenberg, Carol Edelstein, Helen Eisenbach, Christopher Schelling, Sally Bellerose, and Diane Lederman. Many editors along the way have added behind-the-scenes shaping and pruning, in particular Daniel Jones and Louise DeSalvo. A special shout-out to my own personal literary team: Helen Eisenbach, who edits everything I write (often many times), and my agent, Christopher Schelling, who sings me songs. Finally, I am ever grateful to have Engine Books' Victoria Barrett on my side; she makes me one of the luckiest writers in the world.

Printed in the USA
CPSIA information can be obtained
at www.ICGtesting.com
CBHW020029181223
2721CB00005B/381